FISH PIE IS WORSE THAN CANCER

Best wishes

Karen Nimmo

Kevin Norquay

Cover design by Chris Jones,
Graphetti Design

Fish Pie by Kiva Atkinson

Book design and production by
DIYPublishing.co.nz

Published by onthecouch
onthecouch.co.nz

ISBN 978-0-473-29592-9

FISH PIE IS WORSE THAN CANCER

A true story of love, hope and rat-like cunning

KAREN NIMMO

Also by Karen Nimmo:
My BUM Looks BRILLIANT in This
The one true secret of lasting weight loss

AUTHOR'S NOTE

Before you read this, there are two things you need to know about me: I'm a psychologist and I'm a competitor. I like to win.

So when cancer came to our place I wanted to beat it, not just physically but mentally. I wanted to arm us against the mind games of the disease because that's where I had seen people struggle the most.

The medical profession has yet to fully confront the mental damage cancer inflicts: the dark thoughts and feelings, the rollercoaster emotions, the fear that jabs at you in the middle of the night. Doctors go after cancer physically — with scalpels and drugs and radioactive beams. They're good at that, yet it just isn't enough if you want to survive the emotional turmoil as well as the march of the mutant blood cells.

This book is our family's cancer story. While the events recorded are accurate in time and place, I've changed some people's names and identifying details to protect their privacy.

The story is based on a journal I kept that year to help me make sense of things, a safe place to offload my thoughts and feelings as we plotted our way forward (for a shortcut to our best tips see the Roadmap at the back of the book). If it helps even one person, or family, I'll be happy. But I'd be lying if I claimed to have written it for some grand, higher purpose. This was simply my therapy. I wrote it for my family; I wrote it for myself.

KAREN NIMMO

FEBRUARY 2015

WITH THANKS

This book is dedicated to the person who anonymously left the fish pie on our doorstep. You represent everyone who loved, helped and supported us. We are truly grateful. And I still have your pie dish.

"The greatest wealth is health."

Virgil
Roman Poet, 70BC–19BC

CONTENTS

MOONHAWKS

1959

The game was Vets and Cows. It took place on a sun-dappled lawn, ringed by prickly barberry hedges and tucked in the corner of a 100-acre Waikato dairy farm. The days were long and warm.

The little girl was six and played the lead role of the cow. Her three-year-old brother was the vet; he had a satchel full of wooden clothes pegs for medical tools. The cow laughed and fell to the ground, writhing in fake agony. The worried vet hovered over her with his pegs. Their mother, a new baby boy in her arms, watched from the sewing room, smiling.

They were best friends, the cow and the vet, there was no-one else, there was no pre-school in the 1950s and their nearest neighbours were outside the range of a toddler's legs. She invented all the games and he followed; they played together for hours.

And then the cow was gone. There one day, missing the next, dead from complications following a routine appendix operation. The sutures had burst, the internal bleeding was not stopped. She never left the hospital.

"She's an angel now," the little boy was told.

"She's gone to live in Heaven."

The house fell silent, heavy, the impact of loss not understood. His father worked longer hours in the dairy shed. His mother tended the baby, scrubbed the floors, put meals on the table.

A crack opened in the young relationship.

The boy began to have nightmares. Moonhawks — huge, black-winged creatures from his imagination — swooped down on him. He ran and ran, but ropes held him back. He woke up screaming so often that his parents sought medical advice.

He was admitted to hospital for tests; he was scared and homesick, nurses ignoring his requests for drinks and his pleas to go home. He passed the physical and psychiatric tests, perhaps because he hadn't given them the answers they wanted; perhaps because he was a model of sanity compared with the boy in the next bed. That boy slashed holes in his mother's raincoat with scissors.

He was discharged from hospital. Nothing more was ever said, the experience buried. He began to get stomach aches. Sometimes they led to vomiting and days off school. His mother began to worry about his ability to cope with stress. Occasionally, as he built a successful career in journalism, he did too.

Back home, the days on the farm rolled by. The sun still shone. There was no more Vets and Cows. The boy played alone, with his rugby ball, instead.

Chapter 1

THE GOLFER

Kev's most challenging round began on a clear morning in winter 2012. Looking back, we should have known it was serious. Shoving anti-flam capsules in your anus to get through 18 holes of golf isn't what most people do on a Sunday morning.

Kev was a golfer, hooked on the game since he first swung a club at the age of forty. Rain, sleet, howling Southerlies, he played in them all. When frost dusted the fairways, he switched from a white ball to a coloured one so he could still see where it landed. When none of his regular buddies were available, or when they bailed due to storm warnings, he played by himself.

"Surely not today," I'd say, drawing the duvet over my head as rain hammered on the roof.

"That's what I have wet weather gear for." He'd pull a rain slicker over his head and bang the front door behind him.

I liked a round of golf but I didn't feel it like Kev did; it didn't make my heart thump. He said he was chasing possibility. The chance that every time he stepped out on a course something incredible could happen.

Every game is a story, he said. "Every hole is a chapter, every ball a page. You just have to let it unfold." It was the nearest he got to philosophy.

Then one Sunday the front door didn't slam.

When I got up I found him down the back of the house in the half light, sitting gingerly on the edge of the couch and flicking through a golf magazine.

"My back's a bit sore. I might take it easy today."

He turned sideways, lifted his legs slowly up onto the couch and eased back against the cushion. His normally tanned face was pale beneath dark stubble.

I drew up the blind in the living room. The grey light revealed a clear, windless morning. Perfect golf conditions.

Over on the couch Kev had his eyes closed. His magazine had fallen onto the floor.

That's when I felt the knot in my stomach fan into fear.

What's really going on? I thought.

It began nine months earlier with a twinge in his back. A twinge, which morphed into a stabbing, lingering pain that for medical insurance purposes we wanted to claim as an accident, except there hadn't been an accident. There was no trauma, no strain, no clear point of origin. It was just a dull ache that roared up then receded like the tide, tricking us into thinking it was simply the product of a dodgy golf swing.

He went to a doctor. Then another. He had examinations. He had x-rays.

Nothing.

Bad posture, possibly. A high pressure job. An office chair with poor ergonomics.

He did core-strengthening exercises with anatomical names: the single-leg abdominal press; segmental rotation; quadruped extension. We renamed them, laughing: The Alligator Roll. The Flamingo Stretch. The Bonking Dog. The pain went away. Then it surged back, white hot, forcing him to pace the house through the early hours of the morning. Some nights he couldn't lie down, snatching sleep as he sat upright on the sofa.

"It's nothing sinister," one back specialist said, inhaling $300 and rubber-stamping a few sessions of physiotherapy.

"Poncy git," Kev said, dismissing the specialist's manner and his findings. "I was just another wallet walking in the door."

But something was wrong. He was tired all the time. He fell asleep between arriving home from work and dinner. Then again after dinner. He began to cough, hacking like an old man in the mornings, a dry bark that wouldn't shift.

At night he'd sweat, not always, but his pillow gradually stained yellow. His stomach burned with acid reflux.

More medical appointments for symptoms that played Hide n Seek, each of them daring each other to present at the same time to fill out the picture. They refused: as his stomach problems flared, his backache retreated. The cough and sweats came and went, mounting fatigue was pinned on the demands of a stressful job and our busy lives.

Then one Saturday he went for a walk, a test for leg muscles he kept saying were losing their power.

"I'm wading through cotton wool," he said, stumbling in the door. "I can't feel my feet hitting the ground".

The next day he couldn't stand up long enough to poach eggs. He tripped on a cushion lying on the floor because his feet wouldn't obey his brain's orders to lift them. Extra-strength painkillers couldn't stifle the pain in his back.

Even then, the registrar at the emergency orthopaedic clinic indicated he was being dramatic, yanking and twisting his legs, applying pressure to his back until he gave in.

"Argghhhh," Kev let out his breath. I jumped back, startled, he was normally uncomplaining about pain.

"It's not life-threatening," the doctor said, crouching in front of us, yawning. "You just need to manage your pain medication better. Here's some codeine, take it regularly. Come back if it gets worse."

He ripped a sheet off his prescription pad, stood up and turned away. Kev and I stared at his back wondering how we were going to get all the way down to the car park.

By morning I had to help him out of bed.

He winced with pain as I eased his shoes on. I floored the accelerator through the city to get to Wellington hospital. In the Accident and Emergency wait room, I called my clients for the day and cancelled their appointments. "Small family emergency," I said. "I'll be in touch to reschedule."

"Fine with me," said one woman, who had been addressing her procrastination issues in therapy. "I'm happy to put things off for a while. Take all the time you need." She laughed at her own joke and I smiled.

"Kevin Norquay," the nurse called, and I forgot all about work.

In the examination room, people wearing navy blue scrubs were walking faster, talking faster. There were more tests, bloods and urine, x-rays, rapid sign-off for expensive scans, spinal taps, probes.

More doctors, each wave of a higher rank than the previous one. More questions. An uneasy feeling they were showing way too much interest for it to be a slipped disc. Must be a really complicated nerve compression, we thought. Or perhaps a bone problem?

The diagnosis came at nightfall.

The lights in the ward had been dimmed; Kev lay alone in his hospital bed, heavily dosed with pain medication. As his eyes shuttered, a doctor he had not seen before appeared in the doorway of his room: a young man in a long white jacket, unshaven, pouches under his eyes. He wore a hospital identity tag but he didn't introduce himself. He didn't mention cancer. He just stood at the side of the bed and threw all the other scary words together in one sentence.

"Tumour…malignant…spine….paralysis."

Then the kicker: Secondary. The medical way of saying the cancer had spread.

For a few seconds Kev wondered if it was all some kind of sick joke.

It wasn't. A joke would have been welcome.

The doctor left.

Kev fell back on his pillow, the course of his life forever altered.

A medical diagnosis is just a clump of words. The person who receives it is in the same physical condition as they were minutes, days, sometimes months before the conversation between doctor and patient takes place. But the combination of medical tests and clinical opinion bring the curtain down on uncertainty and hurl you into a new place psychologically, an uneasy combination of knowledge and dread.

So he had a label, a name for his story. Something to help him make sense of the past few months, the past year even. There's not much heroism in saying "I'm tired, I have a sore back and my legs have lost a bit of power lately."

But when you give that cluster of symptoms a name?

Well, "spinal cancer" is a big label. It's a way of taking

what's going on out into the world. It's like naming a baby. Suddenly this thing has a life, a personality, a presence.

Suddenly you have a way of scaring people; suddenly you have a way of scaring yourself.

That's why it is a hefty chunk of information to carry into the night when you are alone in a hospital bed. Especially when you had started the day believing one of your spinal discs had blown out.

Kev found his cellphone in the bedside drawer and called me. I'd left him for the night believing we wouldn't know any more until the specialist made his morning rounds.

The landline telephone was ringing as I walked through the front door, the house breathing a winter chill, our 17 year-old-daughter Tess trailing behind me.

"Malignant," I heard him say. "Tumour." I didn't hear the words in-between.

The blue formica of the kitchen bench rose to meet me as I slumped on it. Cancer.

Cancer. Cancer. Cancer.

What to do? What to do at 10pm on a Monday night when you have just had news that trumps everything else in your world?

Just one thing. One phone call. It was to our elder daughter Kate, who was 19 and living in a flat in town.

Should I leave it till morning to tell her in person?

I spied the cell phone clutched in her little sister's hand and I decided I didn't want a worried text message to beat me. Not with this news.

I heard the break in Kate's voice. She sniffed. I knew she

was crying. Do your children ever get to an age when you don't want to be the one mopping up their tears?

I swallowed. "Do you want me to come and get you? Stay with us for the night?"

Kate's voice leveled out. She was a steady person. "I'll be okay. I'll come to the hospital with you in the morning. Pick me up?"

"It'll be early." I knew Kate didn't rise early from choice. "I want to be there at 7am when the doctor does his rounds."

"Come on Kazza," she said, as if I hadn't given her credit for clocking the seriousness of her dad's condition.

"I'll be ready at 6.30. Text me when you're outside," she said.

So I took my fear to bed. Tess slid in next to me and held my hand.

"It'll be ok," I wanted to tell her, but the words wouldn't come. I squeezed her hand and we lay silent, staring into the darkness.

The hours ticked and I muttered a prayer: to God, the Universe, to anyone listening. It crossed my mind this was vaguely hypocritical when Kev was not religious and I'd long neglected my spirituality in the whirl of ordinary life. Still, I reasoned we were going to need all the help on offer. And, as I lay there, wide-eyed and incapable of sleep, I thought this: it must be easier to be an atheist in the daylight.

THE NEWSROOM

*F*lashback. *It's Autumn, 1990, the newsroom of The Dominion morning newspaper where I'm employed as a sports reporter.*

I have the day off but I've come in to grab something from my desk. My friend Steph, who is visiting from Dunedin, is with me. The newsroom is buzzing, the chief reporter swearing, the early afternoon adrenalin palpable as the news crackles and breaks.

I show her around, pointing out the various clusters of desks: business, finance, politics, features and, finally, sports. Home to seven men and me.

As I talk, Steph scans the room, her expression blank; current affairs don't interest her, gossip does. So do men.

"Who's the guy who's been giving you a hard time?" she says.

I hesitate. Kev's there, sitting with his head down and scanning a newspaper. He's the rugby league and track specialist on the desk; I'm in charge of netball and tennis. The day before he'd told me he'd seen an advertisement for auditions for the lead role in a horror movie — why didn't I try out?

"If you don't like my face don't keep looking at it," I'd spat back.

"Sorry," he'd mumbled, red-faced. It wasn't a malicious comment. Just a dumb joke. Just a guy trying to get attention.

He hears us now: two female voices in the sports department is a siren. He has short crow-black hair swept across his forehead, a black slug of a moustache filling a deep top lip. Big aqua-blue eyes, thick dark eyelashes. Lashes that had led to a lifetime of being told they were wasted on a male.

Today he's wearing a pink long-sleeved shirt, branded with a Lacoste alligator logo; tight grey corduroy pants that, when he stands up, will be slightly too short at the hem. A red sweater hangs over the back of his chair. Colour co-ordination is not his strength. He looks like a 1980s highway patrol cop on a day off.

I introduce Kev by his newsroom name "Norks", the obvious abbreviation for Norquay. Steph smiles at him: she likes sports, especially male sports, and they chat. I feel strangely left out. I wander over to my desk, pick up and pen and fiddle with it. I remember Steph had once stolen a boyfriend from me. Well, not actually stolen. She'd just moved in on a guy in a bar I'd been talking to. But — still — she was better looking than me. You wonder.

"What did you think of him?" I fling the words over my shoulder as we leave the newsroom, heading for the elevator. I punch the down arrow. I'm trying to be casual, disinterested.

"Norks?" she says, and her use of his nickname jars.

"Yes," I jab the down arrow again.

Steph waits until I look over at her, and then she winks.

"Nice eyes," she says.

Chapter 2

THE PATIENT

"Let's go," the hospital orderly said, jerking Kev's bed onto its rollers and spinning him out the door of the orthopaedic ward. I picked up my bag and followed, almost having to run to keep up. What's the rush? I was still trying to process my shock at the sharp jag in the trajectory of my life.

A day earlier I had been standing in my kitchen wondering whether I had the ingredients to make chicken lasagna. Now I was race-walking beside a hospital bed, hoping that a massive blast of radiation might be enough to save my husband's legs.

Happiness is such a relative thing. When things are going well, you push the boat out. You dream big. You think about what you would do if you won a million dollars. You think about overseas holidays, new houses, new cars; new golf clubs if you are Kev, new Italian leather boots if you are me.

When life is hard, though, things become a whole lot simpler. Bad news has a way of dumbing down your aspirations very, very fast.

To a place where just getting to the end of the day is a triumph.

The tumour had weaved through the spine, squeezing the nerves and cutting off the mobility south from his lower back. It was a very good explanation for not being able to stand up.

The radiologists slid him onto a table, measured him up, covered him with crosses to mark the target areas and trained powerful radioactive beams on him.

Sitting outside the door, staring glassy-eyed at the outdated magazine on my lap, I could hear him talking Super Rugby to the staff who'd been called back after hours to do this urgent treatment. His legs might have lost their power, but his voice hadn't. He was cheerfully talking up the chances of the Waikato Chiefs, the province he had supported since boyhood with the blind loyalty of an English football fan.

I heard the banter. I heard the laughter.

Then I heard a nurse next to me giving directions to the oncology library on the third floor.

"Who's got cancer?" I wondered vaguely.

My mind flipped back to a time when I was fresh out of

University and in the supermarket when I heard a woman telling her little boy to mind out for the lady. And I'm a little startled as I realise she's talking about me. I'm 21. In the eyes of the world I'm all grown up, I'm a *lady*.

That's what hit me, suddenly, as the magazine slipped from my knee. That I was sitting in the oncology radiation suite for a very good reason. That the person with cancer in their family was me.

Malignant tumours are born out of manic abnormal cell growth. As these cells divide and multiply, lumps of tissue form and swell until they interfere with the body's systems and function. These original, or primary, tumours only kill people about 10 percent of the time. Secondary tumours, those that form when destructive cells set off around the body, do the rest. When tumours spread, destroying other healthy tissues and going after other organs, the cancer is said to have metastasised.

When that happens, you are in trouble.

That's where Kev was. Knowing he had cancer. Knowing it had travelled. Waiting to find out the destinations.

The worry was fierce. We knew the odds if there was cancer in certain places, like the brain or the liver or the lungs or the pancreas. It was not a bright picture. Kev said he was not thinking about dying, but he unnerved me by repeatedly saying he'd had a good life.

"Better than I could have imagined," he said.

"If it was to end now I'd be ok with that."

I was not sure I would, but I let him talk, just in case.

My mind wandered. I wondered if I'd be living in our house on my own by the end of the year. Responsible for two grown daughters. Incapable of driving all the remote controls in our lounge. Unsure of which day or week to put the yellow and green recycling bins out. Guilty for even letting selfish, practical concerns find space in my head.

The primary site turned out to be the stomach. This news was delivered by a fresh-faced registrar who gave away that she was the bearer of bad tidings by spending five minutes talking about the weather and her weekend events before getting nervously down to business.

"There have been some findings..."

Findings. Medical jargon for things you won't want to hear.

She was a sweet kid: an orthopaedic trainee who came to work this week expecting to deal with broken legs and crocked backs.

"There's a tumour in your stomach," she said. "The cancer started there and has eaten through into your back..." I watched her swallow. This was almost certainly her first professional brush with cancer and her eyes pooled with tears as she forced the words out into the sterility of the ward. There was no training good enough for this job. I understood that, you have to learn by doing it. I patted her shoulder in comfort; I couldn't quite manage a hug though.

Once on our own, Kev and I clasped hands and spilt a few tears. Not many; perhaps each of us realised that breaking down right now wouldn't help the other one. We were in deep. We knew that.

We stopped crying and tried a few swear words. That felt better, bolder. So we threw out a few more.

We talked about how lucky we'd been until now. We didn't talk about all that lay ahead of us. We didn't talk about fighting cancer. Or about finding a cure at a clinic in Mexico. Or about miracles. We just talked about what was — right here, right now — and it helped.

We were lucky Kev couldn't walk. It kept him in hospital. It made him look sick. It meant we got fast tests and fast answers. Most people have to wait for their results. Then wait for a second round of results. Finally, they are called to see the doctor. They turn up and sit on hard-backed chairs where they suck in a sentence or two that radically diverts the course of their lives. Then they have half an hour to ask questions and digest the answers before being dispatched onto the street with a whole new framing of their mortality and having to pick up groceries on the way home.

So I've got cancer. I might die. Do we need bread and milk?

We were spared all that because the cancer had run rampant through his body. Kev could barely wiggle his toes. So he was tucked up in a hospital ward, his own room, the medical equivalent of business class air travel, with winter sun pouring in. The room was fenced by solid, white walls and the long silences were punctuated by busy nurses, delivering medication, emptying catheter bags, injecting and poking, questioning and feeding him.

He was safe.

When I got home at night, I only had to deal with my own fear, not his. Well, mine and everyone else's. That was plenty.

"I'm a blood relative." Tess said on one of those evenings, as I threw together a meal neither of us wanted, would barely eat, or would be able to taste.

"So?" I countered, my tired brain incapable of figuring out where she was going with this.

"I'm going to have to give dad bone marrow, I just know it. I so don't want to do it. I'd rather give a kidney or have open heart surgery I think."

I went to interject with something sensible like "we don't even know what kind of cancer it is yet," but Tess was on a roll. She'd have been researching cancer, either trawling the internet or via details she had picked up by watching back episodes of the TV medical drama *House*. In her busy high-wired mind, she had herself parked up in a hospital bed alongside her father, her bone marrow being leached out to save his life.

"You're going to like owe me forever. You're going to have to buy me so many pairs of shoes it's not funny. They put this badass needle in through your hip and all the way down into the bone. The pain. Oh my god…"

Her face was paler than usual. "I will do it because I am blood." Pause. She was thinking, searching her options. "Are you sure you didn't have an affair to have me mum — then I could get out of it."

I smiled to myself; I couldn't resist teasing her, even with cancer threatening to close us down. "No Tessie. I had an affair to get Kate. But not you — you're the real thing. You're blood."

"I so hate you," she said, but there was no weight beneath her words. We both recognised a joke, even if we didn't quite feel like laughing out loud.

Over the next couple of days we learned Tess's bone marrow wouldn't be required, nor would anyone else's.

Kev had Lymphoma, a blood cancer ripe for spreading because it was easily transported around the body by the lymphatic system. It was Non-Hodgkin's Lymphoma, one of the most common types of the disease, representing 4 percent of all cancers and almost exclusively diagnosed in adults. Its name simply meant that it was not the type of Lymphoma a man called John Hodgkin's discovered. Cancer people were clearly not very inventive with names.

We learned the cancer probably started as a gastric stomach ulcer that turned malignant. It could have been there, dormant, for years. This stomach tumour was indolent, which meant it was the lazy kind, slow to take off. A few months ago, it had upped the pace and was attacking the spine, enclosed nerves, and the future we had planned for ourselves with unabashed vigour.

That spread, from stomach to back, and the position of the tumours in the middle of the body, made his cancer a stage four in severity. That was bad because there was no stage five. We knew enough to know that stage fours didn't offer any sort of *Get out of Jail Free* card.

"Is he going to die?" I asked the oncologist when Kev was taking forever in the bathroom adjoining his room. I'm not sure why I asked this because it was a Russian roulette question: in looking for the security of a "no", I had exposed myself to the potential devastation of a "yes".

But the oncologist sidestepped me neatly, as I knew he would.

"It's metastatic cancer," he said, as if that said it all. Read: any cancer that has spread from the original site raised the odds of an unhappy ending.

"Having it in two sites in the middle of your body is risky because it can travel to a lot of different places from there," he said.

He made the middle of the body sound like a busy airport. Except none of the destinations looked too appealing. Especially not the brain, the most likely and the one everyone kept mentioning.

The doctors kept passing through, loading us with information and in our foggy brains the messages seemed to conflict:

- Be upset because this is cancer.

- Be happy because Lymphoma responds to medical treatment better than many others.

- Be grateful because you're still alive. At the moment.

- Be worried because even if it goes away for a while it will definitely COME BACK.

- Most of all, hear this: THERE IS NO CURE.

Kev boarded a wheelchair for the journey across the hospital to see the haematologist, the blood cancer specialist. I pushed the chair, with my handbag swinging off the back. It occurred to me that the last time I did this the vehicle was a pushchair, the passengers my babies. That seemed like the natural order of things; this didn't feel real. I felt like I was floating slightly above the ground. I jammed the heels of my boots into the shiny floors to hear them click against the surface, trying to ground myself in the present, trying to reassure myself that this was real life — my life.

The specialist showed us magnetic images from the scans. We could see clumps of dark cells, shadows buried in healthy tissue, in the back and in the stomach. Then small white crosses, scattered across the images. Those areas were the oesophagus, lungs, liver.

"What do those crosses mean?"

"Shadows, areas of cell mutation, places to watch," he said.

Silence, as we both tried to count them. We couldn't, they were like snow.

"Does this mean the cancer...that it's everywhere?"

The specialist swallowed as he swivelled his chair back to face his computer.

The moment hung.

Then Kev rushed into the silence, grabbing this moment to reveal his biggest fear. That's when I realised that for him cancer — even with its looming death threat — was always going to be the secondary. His legs were the primary.

The golfer was back. He wiggled his toes and looked hopefully up at the specialist.

"Will I be able to walk again?"

Chapter 3

THE PSYCHOLOGIST

You will have figured out that I married Norks, the reporter with the nice eyes. Not to beat off any challenge from my hovering friend Steph, more because he had a big heart, a quick, offbeat mind and we could spend eight hours in a car together chatting and laughing, free of angsty, awkward silences.

What is love, anyway?

Back then, in my twenties, it seemed simple: I just knew what I liked versus what I did not; who I wanted to be with versus who I did not. And, perhaps, when you strip away the complexities, that's all love is: wanting to be with someone — or not wanting to be without them.

Kev was a reader, not of novels but just about everything else from maps and comics to music biographies and every word of Tolkien's *Lord of the Rings*. He sucked up random facts and trivia like a vacuum hose, which made him the darling of any school or pub quiz team he ever turned out for. He was loud and opinionated; words sometimes out of his mouth before he'd put them through the Political Correctness filter, which occasionally got him into trouble.

"I didn't get the job because I'm fat and ugly," a female colleague once said to him, looking for empathy.

"No," he replied. "Surely those weren't the only reasons."

See what I mean?

Aside from sport, he loved Monty Python, bad puns and a mind-blowing range of music — but he had no rhythm for dancing and he couldn't sing to save his life. A shared enthusiasm for watching rugby tests in the middle of the night, though, sealed the deal.

"Of course," I said, when he asked me to marry him after just three months together. A passion for rugby was possibly the only non-negotiable on my checklist. I'd once dropped a guy who didn't tick that box because I didn't want a lifetime of watching rugby tests on my own. Actually I didn't even want one winter. Call me shallow, but you have to look out for your own needs.

But something about Kev reeled me in. I loved him. His consistency, his kindness and his stupid sense of humour.

I loved how much he loved me.

The tight corduroys, pink shirt and highway patrolman's moustache all had to go though.

We wanted to be parents. On our first wedding anniversary a fat, three-month-old baby girl gurgled up at us as we ate fish and chips on our lounge floor, watching sport on television. On our second, I was newly pregnant with our second daughter. Life turned into a tangle of chubby hugs, mushy food, caravan summers at the beach. We collected things: shells, leaves, snails, memories.

Then towns and houses. We moved from the city to the provinces in search of a more relaxed, less expensive way to raise a family. Restless, we moved back to the city again. Wellington this time, New Zealand's capital city.

Kev continued to build his career in journalism; I stayed home with the kids, freelance writing around their sleep times to help pay the bills, stories about the dangers of baby walkers, the rocketing price of butter, a sweet old man who crocheted poems into tea towels (who was later outed as a paedophile), celebrity dogs and haircuts. I wrote a car column, a sports column, filled glossy gossip pages for women's magazines.

Kev's job took us to London for a year. We backpacked around Europe hauling the girls through cathedrals, ancient ruins and landmark statues, on a mission to find hot chips in every European city, a nod to Kate's culinary preferences at the time. Actually, at any time before or since. At night we jammed into cheap hotel rooms, writing family journals, picnicking on bunks, playing charades, laughing at each other.

Then we returned home and I went back to university. It wasn't an "aha moment". Just an itch to try something new before middle age tightened its grip, rather than persist with a journalism career that had run out of gas as it competed with my kids for attention.

But the moment I stepped into Victoria University's psychology department, something I still don't fully understand, I felt my heart rate speed up. Or slow down. Or something.

"Did you find anything interesting down there? Kev asked that evening.

"There's a paper I'd like to do."

"Great, when do you start?" he said, always the champion of my cause, always wanting me to do whatever made me happy.

I smiled but I didn't tell him the whole story. I hadn't just found a paper; I'd found something I knew would absorb me for the rest of my life.

One semester turned into five years. I kept freelance writing for as long as I could, squirrelling away as much cash as I could to pay my fees. I studied hard. It made me happy, it made us poor.

When my guilt kicked in, Kev smothered it. "Do it," he said, shouldering the financial load. "Keep going. You love that stuff."

I did. A ticket to explore the deep dark caves of the human condition. A job that wasn't work. A calling, not a career. Perhaps. Who knows? But I felt like I could breathe out. It was a sort of homecoming.

I interned in a Hospital psychiatric ward, turning up with carefully prepared questions on a neat clipboard to assess a man named Steven. Steven, who was in the High Security lock-up, had wildly matted hair and caked dirt under curly, 10cm long fingernails. He'd been living in the bush for months.

"I'm Karen," I stammered. Asking what had brought Steven here, and what his therapeutic goals were, suddenly didn't seem all that appropriate.

He bared his teeth.

"Raaaaaaarrrrrrr," he howled. Recoiling, I backed up against the wall, hugging my clipboard. My eyes popped. Welcome to the other side.

I interviewed young men who swore they had insects under their skin, crawling up and down their arms, anorexic girls fragile, skeletal and frightened by lolly cake, a young man who tried to hang himself on his bed end with his shoelaces.

And many more. A schizophrenic man who stood with one arm raised above his head at parties, a woman who wore only army fatigues in case war broke out around her house, a 10-year-old boy whose first words to me were "get the fuck out of my face."

Other peoples' lives.

My psychology classmates, too, had their stories. Abuse. Disability. Depression. Family difficulties and mayhem. Big, valid reasons for why they had wanted to study clinical psychology. It was a long way from the world I'd been raised in. I knew nothing of mental illness, not in a formal sense.

Sure, I'd had my problems, stresses and challenges. I'd had to move towns and schools more often than I'd have chosen; I'd been bullied, as kids with red hair and freckles always are, and I'd been the target of some nasty teenage girl exclusion tactics. But I had not known real despair, I had not had my emotional reserves drained, then excavated. I hadn't been abused. My parents weren't alcoholics or substance abusers. They had stayed together, and not just for their children. My own still young kids had come through their early years without major illness or trauma. I'd grown up with a different foundation than the people I was working with and, often, alongside.

I thought, all through my studies, it would either make me a very good psychologist — or a very bad one.

And that's what I remembered now as I sat beside the hospital bed, the patient — my husband — prone and exhausted, rogue blood cells going crazy inside him. That my life had gotten tough.

I finally had my test.

*Recovery depends on… "the person's will to live and in
mobilising all the natural resources of the mind and body [and
spirit] in turning back disease."*

Norman Cousins
Anatomy of An Illness

Chapter 4

THE GAME PLAN

"What about my golf show?" Kev said.

He was lying in his hospital bed, four days worth of diagnostic drama, scans, biopsies and tests behind him. He had cancer in two sites, mutating cells and ominous shadows everywhere. He was close to numb from the waist down, he couldn't raise his legs off the bed and his urine trickled continuously into a catheter bag strapped to one wasted leg. He travelled the three meters to the toilet in a wheelchair and he had to be showered sitting down because he couldn't raise the hose nozzle by himself.

He had a bit going on. And all he could think of was his golf show, scheduled for the next morning.

Actually, golf "show" was an exaggerated moniker for the unpaid radio segment he had done at 7.45am every Saturday for the past four years. He would clamber out of bed at dawn to spend two hours preparing, going online to track overnight scores around the world. Then, leaning on his reliable memory, he would chat to Newstalk ZB's host Jason Pine about how all the New Zealand golfers were doing, touch on the antics of all the game's most famous players and tell a few stories. It took between 6 and 10 minutes depending on how many advertisements were queued up for the day.

"What do you reckon? Shall I do it this week or find someone else?"

I paused. The obvious answer to take a break for a few weeks, he had cancer, he was exhausted, he needed all the rest he could get.

But there were bigger things at stake than sleep. And there was more to think about than cancer.

Into my mind jumped Logan Black, a young man I had met at an evening Cancer Society lecture about a year earlier. An internationally recognised oncologist was visiting New Zealand to talk about the latest in research and treatment. I had worked with a number of clients with cancer so I'd gone along to hear about any new developments in the psychological treatment of people with the disease.

Yellow balloons were tied to the doors of the lecture theatre. The room was filled with head scarves and hats; people wore plastic daffodils pinned to their tops and jackets. The air felt warm, slightly stagnant; the energy flat. But what did I expect? This wasn't a night out at the movies. You don't come to a cancer lecture unless you have a serious investment in the subject.

I was slightly late and the room was packed.

"There's a seat here," a male voice said. I weaved my way past a couple of sets of bony knees. "Thanks," I said to the man, dropping into the seat beside him, as the speaker began.

The oncologist pumped out facts and figures, her relentlessly positive spin struggling to mask the fact that cancer still strikes — and kills — a startling number of people. Medical advancements had been made: drugs were more sophisticated, people were being diagnosed earlier and living longer (and less painfully). However, cancer remained the leading cause of death in New Zealand, responsible for a third of all deaths annually.

Treatment, as she described it, was still encased in a medical model: go after the cancer — either eradicate it or hammer it into retreat. It was based on a three-pronged regime (surgery-radiation-chemotherapy) in various combinations.

The psychology of the illness — possible cause, triggers, how to deal with it and the FEAR of everything associated with it — was largely ignored.

I began to wish I'd stayed home with a glass of wine.

The oncologist took a break, reaching for a tumbler of water. People in the audience began to ask questions, reaching for answers, a way forward.

Beside me, my neighbour squirmed in his seat. I looked across and saw him in the dim light. I placed him in his early to mid-thirties, slim, dressed in a dark business suit and blue-striped open-necked shirt. Clean shaven but with the bluish shadow of a day's growth. Short dark hair, spiked on top. He didn't look like the majority of people in the room. A GP, perhaps? Or the son of a cancer patient?

Seeing me look over he apologised for getting restless: "Can't sit still," he said. "I've been to way too many of these things."

He introduced himself. Logan Black's eyes shone, his skin was a healthy tan, he spoke with force. We chatted: I told him I was a psychologist and he told me he was terminally ill.

I tried to hide the surprise on my face and he laughed.

"Do I need a beanie and a walking stick for you to believe me?"

He waved a hand lightly towards the audience, who were clustered in small groups, chatting in low tones. "Look what cancer does to people," he said.

"It backs them into a corner. Takes away their power. A lot of them are too scared to move."

I knew what he meant. I could feel it in the room: it wasn't desperation, it was helplessness. Psychologically, I knew anxiety was typically supposed to set up a fight or flight response: to stand up to the fear or to run from it. But there was another option. To freeze. That's what cancer can do: put you in the freeze zone. Make you wait for others to help you, make you depend on things or people outside yourself.

Freezing — shutting down — was dangerous, he said. It was the most interesting thing I'd heard all night.

After the lecture I saw Logan again, chatting in the foyer. He seemed to know everyone. There was a queue forming to talk to him. I wasn't surprised. If there was a poster boy for terminal illness, he had to be it. I wanted to know more. So the next day I tracked him down on the Internet and emailed him. A professional request. We met for coffee.

Again, I was struck by his energy, his forthright manner. He was 39 years old and looked nearly a decade younger. It didn't fit with my image of a dying person. Certainly he was doing something right.

Logan told me four years earlier he had been given nine months to live. Melanoma that began as a dot on his thigh continued to spread its fingers through his organs. He'd had pieces clipped off, and out of, his body during multiple surgeries. His body was tracked with scars. Yet he sat across from me now, visibly a picture of robust good health.

I wanted to ask him about his secret but wasn't sure how to phrase it. He helped me out.

"Early on I made a decision to run cancer alongside my life, not to let it run me. That's what you have to do."

"You have to live normally and make cancer accommodate you, not the other way around. You don't give cancer any room. You make it work for every tiny inroad in your life. Hand over the power and it'll shut you down."

I mentioned the battle he must have had to get this far, but Logan stopped me.

"It's not a fight," he said. "Muscle up to cancer and you're in trouble. It'll beat you every time."

I tried to process what he'd said. In theory, I understood about the fight. It would create internal chaos. "I guess a fight, a battle, would put even more stress on a person's already struggling organs — and psyche," I said, sort of thinking out loud.

He looked at me, nodding like I had passed some sort of test.

You have to play cancer like you play chess, he said. "It's a game of strategy. It's about anticipating the moves as best you can, then countering them. Swiftly."

He took a long sip of coffee. A soy latte. Trim milk. Looking after himself, despite all that was behind him, all that lay ahead.

"Cancer only has one approach — and that's to attack. It exploits vulnerability; it goes after your weak spots. When people hang around in shock after a diagnosis they give cancer a massive head start," he explained.

"So what's the best plan," I asked. "Let's say I've just been diagnosed with cancer. What should I do?"

"You don't lie around on the couch feeling sorry for yourself. That's a death sentence."

"It's like mobilising an army. You have to muster all the forces available to you — mind, body, spirit — and get them marching in the same direction. If you do that, cancer will balk, it will have to rethink."

He leaned forward then, intense, willing me to listen. "Mobilise. Go forward with everything you have in you. That's the key."

Suddenly the image of Logan's face vanished and I found

myself back in the hospital ward, standing along side Kev's bed. I looked at him, barely able to sit up, his face pale against his starched white pillow, waiting for an answer about his golf show.

"Mobilise," I thought.

And suddenly I knew how to frame this and what to do: Kev was not a victim or a sufferer or a patient or a potential survivor. He was just a guy who had cancer. Nothing more, nothing less.

Don't hand over the power. Hang onto it. Use it to help you.

"Do the show," I said. "Your legs might be stuffed but there's nothing wrong with your mouth."

"Just make sure the nurses don't need to empty your catheter bag in the middle of it. I'm not sure how that might sound on radio."

Kev laughed. "Can you put a sign on my door?"

"Please do not disturb between 7.45 and 8am. Patient working."

He reached for his iPad. He needed to study the week's scores before he fell asleep. I ran my mental checklist: Enthusiasm. Something to focus on. Something to do.

Mobilising. Body. Mind. And Spirit, a sense of meaning, of hope.

Tick. Tick. Tick.

I pinned the note on the door, picked up my bag and backed quietly out of the ward.

THE BIRTHDAY PARTY

Just after midnight on Tess's third birthday she appears next to our bed, clutching George, her teddy bear, by his bald ear.

"Tessie sick," she says, throwing up all over the duvet. By dawn she's ragdoll floppy, still vomiting and has diarrhea. I coax her to sip a little water. She gags.

"She needs a doctor," I say.

"I'll wake Kate," Kev's voice beside me.

Tess's breakfast birthday party is cancelled. Balloons tied to every chair around the dining table flutter lamely as the door slams behind us. The birthday girl doesn't notice; Kate starts to cry.

Tess spends five days in hospital on a drip, a wan figure, limp and glassy eyed. Doctors probe and test; fluids trickle into her through a shunt in her tiny arm. I sleep in an armchair next to her bed while the possibilities are checked off: meningitis, blood infection, toxic poisoning, heart problems.

Finally, a diagnosis: rotavirus, highly contagious and probably picked up in the sandpit at kindergarten. Then dehydration due to her stubborn refusal to take even a sip of water.

As colour floods back into her cheeks and her eyes begin to focus, my immune system caves, probably with relief. I start to throw up. Tess doesn't see me, she has spied a swing and slide outside the window.

"Playground?" she says hopefully, as I bolt for the toilet.

We come home from hospital on my birthday. The balloons are still tied to the chairs, puckered and sad. I flop onto the couch, exhausted by worry and broken sleep, and close my eyes.

There's a tugging on my arm. Kate is nearly five. Her wide brown eyes stare at me.

"Can we have the birthday party now?" Then an afterthought. "For you mummy — and Tess."

I blink my eyes open. Tess is in the corner stacking and knocking over block towers with her bear George, her birthday forgotten, mine not yet on her radar. All I want is to crawl into bed. The two birthday girls could happily let this one go unmarked. But someone else badly wants a party and her face is almost touching mine, waiting.

A child's anticipation; a mother's sense of duty.

"Sure," I struggle to my feet, feeling the nausea rise with me. "What shall we make?"

But Kate is gone, already running to the kitchen.

"Fairybread!" she yells over her shoulder.

"It's Tess's favourite."

Chapter 5

THE CADDY

"**Y**ou're my caddy," Kev said, sitting up in bed, pillows propped behind him.

He had track marks and bruises up his arms where various needles have gone in, and a plaster over his hand holding the shunt for his IV drip. His face was yellow-grey under the harsh tube lighting.

"Meaning what? Your personal unpaid slave?" I countered. I was perched on the end of his bed, cross-legged and sipping a take-out flat white from the hospital's Wishbone café.

"You lie in bed making demands and I run around filling them. Tempting. But no. Forgive me for passing up that generous job offer."

He chuckled. "I mean that I can't play this game without you."

His reasoning went like this. He, the player, had been handed the cancer card, told to focus on that round, and only that one, until it was done. As his caddy, I was the bag-carrier, the primary supporter, the strategist behind the cancer project. I was tasked with anticipating the obstacles before they reared up in front of us.

He took the hits; the jabs, the scans, the drugs, the radiation burns so heavy it looked like I had ironed his business shirts on his back. I was responsible for everything else: bringing fresh shirts to the hospital, remembering all that the doctors' told us, researching and collating cancer information, fielding calls, keeping everyone informed, fielding more calls, boosting morale, buying groceries, keeping life on the outside NORMAL.

Kev said his job was easier. But he never said he'd rather have his job than mine. Who would? That's the thing about being the partner of the person who has cancer. However bad it gets for you, you can't really say it out loud. Because their gig is worse.

I had mixed feelings about my new job.

I hated being the purveyor of bad news. I hated calling our families to tell them of the diagnosis, my parents, Kev's mum. I worried about telling my father who was just a handful of days out of hospital following a heart attack.

"There's a tumour in Kev's back," I said. "It's malignant."

Then, worrying that I hadn't been clear enough, I dropped

the c word, the one I knew would set off their internal panic alarms.

"Cancer," I said into the telephone, bracing myself for the catch in their voices.

"Jesus," said my Dad. "That's no good." I could tell he was wincing; his voice was steady but I knew that to him a diagnosis of cancer meant it was all over. I had heard his response when he has learned others had the disease. Like his friend Ron, last year.

"He's had it," I heard him say about Ron to my mother. "It's everywhere. Riddled. He'll be gone by Christmas."

He was right about Ron, too.

He didn't say that this time though. He was stoic. For me.

"Do they…." Change of tack. "Can they treat it?" he asked.

"First he's going to have radiation to try and shrink the tumour, get him walking again. Then he'll have chemotherapy." I tried to sound even, pragmatic, task-focused.

Keep talking about what's happening now; not what might be. It was like giving a eulogy at a funeral. You can talk about the past. You can talk about the person. But as soon as you stray into what it means for you and your future you're on trembling ground.

I repeated the same things over and over to family and friends, wearily, robotically.

The questions came at me, sometimes hesitantly, sometimes like a gun being fired in my face. How is he? Where's the cancer? How did it start? What were the symptoms? And — the worst one, the one everyone wanted to know even if they were frightened to ask: *what's his prognosis? Is he going to die?*

The truth is I was afraid of answering all these questions because each time it felt like another emotional jolt for me. But I forced myself to go slowly through the story because they all cared and they were scared too.

"At least we have a treatment plan," I said, leaving it there. I didn't add "he'll be ok" or "we're going to beat this" because I didn't have a clue where we were headed.

And I never wanted to lie, especially not to my kids.

Strange as it sounds, I liked that I suddenly had so much to do. In my other life, the one where I was a psychologist, helping people sort out problems and build better lives, I spent so much time sitting, thinking and listening. It was good to be able to get off the couch, walk around and do things, fetch water and heat packs, run errands and wield the shower nozzle at my victim, as he sat undefended on a plastic stool.

"Hey, watch what you're doing with that thing," he yelled as I attacked.

"What're you gonna do about it Norks? Chase me?"

I felt guilty about this but it was interesting to learn new things. Within days, we were talking a new language, the language of cancer: nil by mouth (no eating), Hickman line (a catheter used for administering substances through the veins) getting a line in (insertion of said line), staging (cancer's seriousness rating) bloods (abbreviated expression for blood tests), platelets (elements in the blood which assist blood clotting), involvement (part of the body where cancer is), MRI (Magnetic Resonance Imaging) and CT (Computerised Tomography) scans, and the like. It struck me how quickly you could feel at ease in land which was unknown to you the previous week.

Suddenly we were learning about the body, about cancer, how it develops, the medical theory about why it set up in a man who had always responded to my light-hearted jibes about the impact of craft beer on his belly: "You won't find many men over 50 in better shape than me."

Ironically, he was saying this as his body quietly filled up with cancer.

But Kev's diagnosis seemed to defy logic, as cancer sometimes does. There was no trace of the disease in earlier generations of his family. Despite my ribbing, he was not overweight. He was fit from all those hours on the golf course. He had never smoked. He was only a light consumer of alcohol. There was no HIV infection, no obvious exposure to chemicals or radiation. Nor had there ever been any physical trauma to the stomach, just a history of digestive weakness, a vulnerability to rich or greasy food or too many beers.

These were the questions asked by the stream of doctors, specialists. But the ones I was waiting for, the psychological ones, never came.

There was no psychological take on cancer, on cause, on anything.

No-one mentioned stress as a trigger.

No-one mentioned emotional trauma as a player, possibly the original source.

No-one asked if Kev was a nervous person or how he dealt with stress.

No-one talked about the mind games of cancer and how to play them.

There was just a promised visit from the hospital social worker and a Cancer Society flyer with a support group and a helpline listed amongst its services. A counsellor's contact details were stamped on the back. But there were no practical tips or coping strategies to kickstart our cancer journey.

"What about the mental — the emotional — side of cancer?" I asked one of the specialists, a short, compact man in a checked jacket with a gentle manner.

"Do you think stress might have kicked things off? Kev was under a lot of pressure at work last year. His company was being closed down and...."

The doctor looked at me as though he had no idea who I was or why I might be practically camping by his patient's bed. He swept his hair back in a weary gesture. His goal was to keep this man alive, to attack the army of out of control blood cells, with whatever combination of radioactive beams and drugs he could come up with.

And, to be fair, with the threat of paralysis looming and a queue forming at the door for his services, I couldn't expect him to stand around talking about work stress and cultivating hope.

But really? Was that it?

As a psychologist, I was intrigued. More than that, I was

troubled. What do people who suddenly find themselves in the stranglehold of serious illness do? What about those who have just been told they are terminally ill?

How do they make sense of it? What do they tell their children, their friends? How do they cope?

All illness, physical and mental, requires — no, demands — consideration of the *whole* person. This isn't a revelation: the ancient Greek philosophers had this one nailed centuries ago, and too many health professionals to count had backed it up over time.

So come on folks, I thought, as I sat in the corner of Kev's room watching the medical wave crash in, relentlessly focusing on staving off death. How do you treat a man for cancer when you don't understand who he is, his history, his people or his lifestyle? In my world it would be like trying to treat a woman for depression when you didn't understand her personality or her way of life?

Sick and struggling people need to know who they are, their strengths and vulnerabilities, and how they operate in the world. They need a story as to why their illness might have occurred, they need to know what might be keeping it going and they need a roadmap to help them get to the other side — regardless of outcome.

So do their partners and families.

But there was no such navigational tool on offer here. I realised we were going to have to invent one.

When the doctors stopped circling Kev's bed I grabbed my journal and scrawled down some ideas — psychology applied to cancer:

Know the problem. Figure out the story.

Things to address:

History: What might have made him vulnerable to cancer (Biology, family genetics and health history, temperament, childhood experiences. Loss?)

Triggers: What might have kicked it off (environmental factors, stress?)

Maintaining factors: What's keeping the illness going? (Ways of operating/coping and what might need to change.)

Protective factors: Personal strengths we can use to counter it.

Lifestyle: nutrition, exercise, relaxation strategies (how to reduce the internal chaos?)

Relationships and support team: who can we count on?

Attitude. Optimism.

Hope. Then I wrote it again, bigger, and circled it.

I sketched a game plan, writing solidly for half an hour then snapped the journal shut. It was time to go home. My brain felt foggy and tired, but there is nothing like walking through a hospital to raise your awareness of your own robust good health. I wandered through the corridors, noting the people in green gowns, hobbling, on crutches, in wheelchairs, hooked up to drips and dragging IV machines behind them.

When you are healthy hospitals make you feel bigger than you are, taller and stronger, more flexible and well-oiled. Perhaps it's just that the inhabitants seem to have been shrunken and disabled by illness, exaggerating the difference between good and poor health.

This gap should make you feel grateful too, but you are too busy dwelling on the darkness to break out the gratitude journal. All you are thinking about is how you are going to clamber back up into the light.

I reached the lift. The door opened to reveal just one occupant: the specialist who I'd seen with Kev a few hours earlier. He'd swapped his checked sport jacket and trousers for short black lycra cycling pants and a yellow and black windbreaker. He was wearing cross-trainers. From his hand dangled a yellow bike helmet.

"Hello," I said, and he jumped slightly. He clearly had no recollection of me nor of the conversation I'd tried to start earlier in the day. I was invisible to him in the ward and he now had no way of placing me.

He blushed slightly and kept his eyes on the lift door. Socially anxious, I thought. Like many health professionals. Masterful with their clinical knowledge, firm in their decisions. But in real life? Shy and sensitive, one of those teenagers who stood awkwardly in the corner at parties.

As I watched him, he seemed to slip from the saintly pedestal that we place medical professionals on when we are desperate for help. I had been on the other end of it: parents placing undeserved faith in me to help their suicidal, psychotic or anorexic children. It was a heavy load, too heavy sometimes.

There, in the falling lift, I just saw a man. A nice, ordinary man on his way home, to his own life, his own problems. As his status leveled out, I felt mine rise.

In that moment I felt more in control of the situation, more sure of my own knowledge and the plan we would put in place.

Doctor, not God.

By the time the lift hit the ground floor, I was smiling.

"Goodnight," I said to the man with pale skinny legs who was trying to save my husband's life.

He nodded politely and waited for me to exit the lift.

"God wouldn't be seen dead in lycra," I said to myself.

Chapter 6

FAIRY BREAD AND FLAT BALLOONS

The first few days passed quickly. A routine set up. Kev's days were busy, filled with tests and scans and visits from physiotherapists, occupational therapists, social workers, family, friends and colleagues.

"I'm obese," he revealed after being wheeled back from an MRI Scan. "Can you believe that? I'm a small, obese man. I nearly didn't fit in that tube. Why don't they build them bigger? What happens to big Pacific Island guys who need a scan?"

So much to do. So much to learn.

My days were framed by twice daily visits to the hospital: early mornings to read the newspaper his boss John Crowley delivered daily, help him shower and shave and start up the day; evenings to keep him company through dinner and set up the night. We agreed, the darkness was tough: between midnight and 4am was when the ghosts partied hardest in our minds.

In the daytime, though, he was relentlessly cheerful. In his own words: radiant. It was a word he'd adopted a few years earlier as a strategy to lift the mood of his staff.

"How are you Norks?"

"Radiant," he'd reply, beaming.

I thought it made him sound like a pregnant woman but he'd owned it. It surprised people and it made them laugh. And, I had to admit, radiant was perfect in the cancer arena.

He answered waves of emails and text messages, the funny, dark, newsroom humour of journalists. The messages about the "wild sickie" he was throwing made us laugh and cry, they gave Kev a vehicle for his own humour as he answered every one of them.

"Laughter is the best medicine, although technically medicine is the best medicine," wrote one journalist. We filed that one.

Kev kept tapping at the keyboard, light-hearted news bulletins to colleagues, daily updates to family, messages to friends. It took his focus outside of himself, beyond the uncertainty of the day and whatever lay up ahead.

Hi folks, he wrote to his Fairfax buddies.

Thanks so much for all the digital love: the emails, texts and the card.

They have kept me entertained, amused and uplifted — just as importantly they've buoyed my family.

Yes I have encountered turbulence, but I am still flying. Somehow the doctors have managed to string together my four least favourite medical terms and apply them to me. Me! Who never gets as much as a cold!

People keep turning up to prod, needle, scan, radiate and probe. I have never felt so interesting.

Actually the hospital people have been utterly brilliant, and some have even come back on call to tend to me. I'm special, I guess. I'm scared to tell them I'm a journalist!

I'm lucky really. It's a nice day and I have a room of my own with a view. If people would stop jabbing me and forcing me into dark tunnels that make loud noises it could almost pass as a holiday.

Please send any emails even if you have to make them up, and I will pretend to deal with them, just like I do when I'm at work.

I am working, by the way. I have just filed "man discovers feeling has returned to penis when newly mobile legs get entangled in catheter tube."

Look after yourselves, Norks

A master in the art of small talk, he chatted to the doctors, nurses, orderlies. He learned their names, their partners and kids names, their countries of origin. One shift rolled into the next. Hello. Goodbye. Hello. More notes added to his chart.

Just like the email writing, this focus on other people was psychologically helpful: it kept his mind from turning in on itself; on eating itself alive.

"I think some of the patients in this place must be whingers," he said. "The staff seem to get a shock when I ask them about themselves."

When the nurses were not hovering, he practised wiggling his toes and tried unsuccessfully to do leg raises off the mattress.

Groups of intern doctors crowded around his bed asking to play voodoo with his legs.

- Poke this guy with a needle and see if he reacts.
- Guess this man's diagnosis: he can't walk and he can't feel big chunks of his legs.

They stuck needles in him under a blanket.

"Can you feel that? Does it feel sharp or blunt?" they asked.

He grinned blankly up at them, waiting. "Have you done anything yet?"

The interns tried to figure it out. They guessed a compressed disc in his back, or nerve damage. I saw them flinch when he revealed the truth. The word cancer scared people, even fledgling doctors.

With a reporter's curiosity and a love of passing on knowledge, Kev soaked up the attention. He did demonstrations for the interns, day or night. So they kept coming. Waves of trainee doctors, as eager to see sudden, serious cancer up close as I was to see a psychotic episode when I was doing my clinical psychology training.

But now that it was my husband as Medical Exhibit A, I resented it. I didn't like the intrusion. I hated him being a freak show. I hated hearing the story, over and over again: the symptoms we'd missed, the trauma of the diagnosis, the unfolding of a potentially gloomy future. I didn't want to be the wow factor in anyone's education, the case that young doctors talked about for years because it was such a cool story.

But Kev — he loved being the story.

"Bring it on," he said, as another group entered the room.

"If it helps people learn," he said, "I'm in."

People poured in, many ignoring the hospital visitation hours. I was grateful for them because the visits, the laughs, lifted Kev's mood. He liked to talk so he drew comfort from the endless stream of social contact.

"It's actually fantastic to have this much time for people," he said after a regular fat-chew with his mate and colleague Greg Tourelle. "I can't move so I get to sit here and have proper conversations with all the people I care about."

He received everyone with great warmth, he answered all their questions. But I couldn't listen. I couldn't hear the story without dread welling in my stomach. I couldn't bear my guilt when people asked why we hadn't gone to the doctor more or had an MRI scan way back. I couldn't handle the concern on their faces, the careful, caring questions.

I went in search of a coffee while Kev sat up in bed, perky, the hero of his own story and, in a weird way, I was jealous of that. Not the attention, that's not me. I was jealous that his life was so contained, that he had the safety of the hospital walls around him. That he didn't have to get out of bed, go out into the world and go into our local supermarket and be me, "that poor woman whose husband is going to die."

I'm not a weepy person. And over the years I've trained myself not to tear up at my clients' stories, no matter how sad. Way back when I was doing my clinical training a supervisor told me: "don't you ever f'ing cry in front of the clients....it doesn't help. It's their session, not yours." And, so, whether it was the right strategy or not, I've tried to stick to that.

Empathy without tears.

But every evening of those first few days, as I drove home from the hospital in the dark, tears stung my eyes, wet my cheeks.

Fear. Fatigue. Self-pity.

"It's not what happens, it's how you react that counts," I counselled myself as I drove, lines I'd rolled out to clients over the years. "You are in charge of your own response." Platitudes, even to my ears, but I forced myself to follow my advice.

I cried for 4.3 kilometres and then, at the Kelburn pizzeria, I stopped. I turned off the tap, so that Tess, waiting for me with her grandparents, wouldn't feel my fear, would know she had a safe place to land. I was surprised I could control emotion like this, but I could.

At home, the telephone rang and rang. Messages loaded up the voice mail. I listened but I couldn't answer many of them. Not yet. My lawns were cut. Flowers appeared at my front door. My house got cleaned. My fridge filled up with delicious food I could not face. I moved it across to the freezer.

Tess leant on the bench, watching me lift up a potato-topped dish covered with clear wrap. It had been sitting on the doorstep when I got home. There was no note, perhaps by design, or maybe the wind had blown it away.

"Is that a fish pie?" Her voice was loaded with suspicion. She was allergic to seafood.

"Yup," I slid the pie dish into the fridge. "Sure is. Fresh today. Yum."

"Seriously? Are you kidding me?

"No, I'm not."

"But mum! I mean, fish pie is worse than cancer!"

We laughed, it broke up the brick of low mood that had settled on the house. It sounded brittle though and bounced off the wooden floors back at us. It seemed to me that you could still laugh with cancer all around you. Just not for long.

Everything we had planned for the next few weeks got cancelled. Just routine things: work, meetings, catch-ups with friends. The party we were going to throw at home for Tess's 18th birthday was not cancelled though. It was just altered beyond recognition, and moved from our house to Kev's hospital ward.

Tess shrugged and said she didn't care.

"House parties are so last year," she said. I knew it was not what she really thought at all.

She slashed the guest list from 40 to 8 and this group of kids gathered in the ward so the man they all called

"Kevvo" could be at the party. I handed out plastic cups of coke and cut up the chocolate cake one of her friends had brought. Someone else had fairy bread in a lunchbox. One of the boys was trailing a puckered blue balloon on a string.

The kids were easy with the cancer thing, they sat all over Kev's bed bantering, and I took photos of them, thumbs up and smiling.

Just to break things up, they hauled him out of bed and took him for a spin through the hospital in his wheelchair. Back in the room we cranked up the iPod dock and the music burst forth. Party time.

A nurse entered the room. " You'll need to turn the music down."

The young woman in the next room with the broken leg had complained.

"Noise control calling? Just like a party at home," Kev quipped. "Except they haven't blown up my speakers this year."

The kids left to go out for dinner and Kev eased back on his pillow, exhausted. "Great party," he murmured.

I reasoned he was saying that just because he was alive for it. It was a terrible party by anyone's standards. But what do you do? I swept up all cake crumbs and dropped the plastic cups in the rubbish bin. The half-flat balloon bobbed in the corner. Kev and I were alone on a Friday night in a hospital ward. I sat on the edge of his bed with a teacup full of flat coke and he fell asleep in my face.

I stared into the vacuum and swung my legs back and forth over the side of the bed. My baby turned 18 today and I was celebrating it in hospital. Flashback. I had done this before. Fifteen years rolled away. Fairy bread and flat balloons.

Circle of life, I thought, and downed my coke.

Chapter 7

THE RUNNER

When I am several months pregnant with our first daughter Kate, Kev takes on a bet to run the Rotorua marathon. He has already clocked up 10 marathons but it is six years since he owned a serious pair of running shoes. His body is a little soft and his leg muscles tight, but he buys some new shoes, plots a training schedule over three months and begins to train.

He recruits a mate and they hit the road most days after work, logging some heavy mileage on weekends.

"Have fun out there," I call from the couch on Saturday mornings, a leave pass to lie on the couch with a magazine, getting fatter.

I didn't know Kev in his running days. But I know running was an obsession all through his twenties, like golf is now, like surfing and rugby and music were in his youth. Like horse racing had been too before he realised a gambling habit might play havoc with his ability to pay a mortgage.

He was not just an active relaxer; he was an intensive one. Whenever he found something that interested him, he would hurl himself at it with a fierceness that seemed to me to defy the whole philosophy of relaxation.

Running had hooked him as a boy, with self-timed circuits of the farmhouse, but he got serious about it at the age of 16. I had seen his running statistics. Every training run, every mile was neatly logged in exercise books, seconds of improvement tracked in spidery ballpoint. I'd heard the stories from his 10 previous marathons. The races where he went out too fast, where his body rebelled at 20km and he hit the wall, vomiting in bushes. I'd heard about the post-race lactic acid buildup so painful that he could barely walk for days.

"Running taught me about life," he said after one Sunday training run, his leg up on a chair with a packet of frozen peas on his temperamental Achilles tendon.

"It tests you. You get out what you put in. If you don't train every day you'll be found out. But if you do a little bit every day you'll make big improvements over time."

"You know," he said, going all uncharacteristically deep on me, "if you break something into bits, you can manage anything."

When May rolls around he is ready. He navigates Rotorua's lake shores in 3 hours, 7.12 minutes. It is nearly 30 minutes slower than his best time; it's a few minutes quicker than he had hoped for.

"That's the race I'm most proud of," he says later, feet up on the bed, beer in hand.

"Why's that?" My mind trawls all the triumphs he'd had as a young man. He'd been a good runner, a Wellington representative. This was a middle aged man's race — and time. A good effort, yes, but surely not the pinnacle of his running career.

"It was the perfect race. I ran with rat-like cunning," he grins.

"That's what you have to do. You have to start at a speed you can maintain the whole way."

He takes a long sip of beer. "If you go out too hard it'll break you. Keep it steady and you can come home strong."

Kev came home from hospital on a Zimmer frame.

Two weeks after his diagnosis, the former marathon man shuffled towards the front door with tiny, agonising steps. My brother Rhys had water-blasted a smiley face into the pavement outside our house. Kev's face lit up as he crept across it.

"It's a good omen," he said.

He was feeling lucky. The heavyweight blasts of radiation had shrunk the tumour in his back enough to ease pressure on the nerves running down his spine. It meant he had a little feeling back in his legs and just enough muscle power to stand up with the aid of the frame. The doctors had discharged him saying it would be two years until we knew how much the nerves would repair and how well he would ever walk. The bit they didn't say was "if cancer doesn't kill you first."

But — for now — we were home.

Cancer had set up shop in his absence and, although I'd been living there, it was like seeing it for the first time, through the eyes of an invalid.

The house was filled with large, unfamiliar plastic objects, reminding me of long ago visits to the toy library. Except these objects weren't toys and we couldn't get rid of them after a week. There was a shower stool, an elevated toilet seat, crutches and a wheelchair. There were large bottles of fluid to settle his stomach, plastic pots to vomit into, boxes of injections to stop blood clots, assorted jars and metal sheets of coloured pills covering the kitchen benchtop.

There were other changes too: Rhys had removed the bathroom door so Kev could get to the toilet and shower on his walking frame. In place of the door my sister-in-law Anne-Marie had hung a navy shower curtain. It didn't reach the floor and it flapped open with the breeze created every time someone walked past.

Tess complained, with good reason. There was no privacy; it was hard to lock a curtain.

She was thrilled with the shower stool (an excuse to relax in the shower and use even more hot water) and the lofty toilet seat, though. In her highest heels she barely had to bend to pee.

"Cancer pro," she announced, emerging from the bathroom. "Loving that seat."

The London Olympics were on and Kev and I watched them together, hours and hours of TV sport: all through the day and at night when we couldn't sleep. It was the first time we'd done this in 12 years: Kev had been a reporter at the previous three Olympics: Sydney, Athens and Beijing. With his vast knowledge of sport, especially track and field, he was usually great company in the fan seat.

But his passion for great sport had vanished: he was quiet and emotional. Easily upset. Weepy. The highs and lows of the Olympics, the feel-good and against the odds stories broke him.

"What the hell is wrong with me?" he eventually said. "I'm even crying at the archery."

"Give yourself a break. It's about time you cried. Crying is part of healing."

"But archery? Come on."

"Fair. Archery is probably going a bit far."

In a practical sense, it was easier to have Kev home. Emotionally, it was much tougher. Hospital was a safe place, a haven: there, our behaviour, our cascading thoughts and feelings, were neatly fenced in by the hustle of hospital staff and activity. Moving home was like having someone snip the wires. Emotions, no longer contained, tore through the fence and we had to find places for them. We had to reframe the way we were going to work this — and we had to adjust to being at home together all day long: him as the reluctant patient, me as his reluctant nurse.

One morning, lolling in his armchair, he pumped up the music, from just loud to blaring. It was a rousing guitar-laced Southern rock song that grated as I did the dishes, mopped the floor, did *everything* around him. While he just sat and watched. I wanted to be patient and loving with the Poor Cancer Guy but that song hit the wrong note — and I caved.

I turned back into myself.

Me: Hey can you turn that music down? Please.

Him: WHAT?

Me: TURN IT DOWN.

Him, sulkily, lowering the volume: When are you going back to work? I was enjoying that.

Me (only just refraining from mentioning that I didn't have a bloody choice about going back to work): Just because you have cancer doesn't mean you can do anything you want.

Him: What's the point of cancer then?

Me: Well it's not to turn into an arsehole.

Uneasy silence.

Note to self: People with cancer still annoy you. Sometimes, they drive you crazy. Cancer doesn't turn them into sweet, grateful Saints. They can play up and push boundaries because they have the best excuse, and you let them because they are sick and THEY MIGHT DIE. That's until you feel sorry for yourself, get mad and fight back.

Where to draw the lines?

How to navigate a whole new world that you did not want but are pretending you are fine with?

Visitors kept knocking at the door. Family. Colleagues. Friends. Bringing things. Books, magazines, DVDs, meals, biscuits, questions, sympathy, kindness. I made coffee. I made more coffee. Then I escaped the house while Kev made coffee, shakily leaning on the kitchen bench, telling the story, our story, over and over as the questions kept coming.

It was more than the questions too, it was dealing with the reactions of other people, packaging up their fear in a pretty box with a neat bow so they didn't have to worry.

I recalled a story my friend Marg had told me from a few years earlier when she had just got out of hospital after a mastectomy.

She'd gone to answer her door.

"Ohhhh I can't bear that you have cancer," sobbed the visitor on the doorstep, collapsing into Marg's arms. "You were one of the people I wanted to grow old with."

"You might still get that chance," said the heavily bandaged Marg, soothing up the weeping woman and making her a cup of tea but mentally putting a line through her name.

"Can you believe that bitch?" she had said, telling the story with such drama that we were both weak with laughter. She made me deal with HER crap about my cancer."

Now I knew fully what she meant. I felt responsible for making other people feel better. When they asked after Kev I gave them what I thought they needed: positive tidbits to snack on and share with anyone else they ran into on the way home:

- Kevin's home again now

- He's eating well

- He's in really good spirits

- His legs are working a little better.

Of course I kept it all sugar-coated. The nasty stuff stayed at home, unfit for public consumption:

- He lay drooling in a chair for most of the day

- His legs look like chicken wire

- His hiccups are so bad they shake him out of his chair

- He's so constipated he had to claw the poos out of his own bum last night.

How would that have gone down? How to freak out the neighbours.

Was I resentful? Angry? Yes, and occasionally it would flare, sometimes unfairly, at comments and clichés that were only people's best efforts at comfort and support.

On the outside I looked perfectly in control, the loving wife and uncomplaining caregiver; inwardly my emotions ran free, sometimes a host of them rearing up within an hour: angry, sad, calm, decisive, confused, worried, agitated, wired, exhausted, steady and scared.

Sometimes, cool and languid. Sometimes, just plain flat. Cheerless. Backed up against a wall with cancer laughing in my face.

When Kate was a little girl she came home one day from kindergarten with a painting. It was a dour mesh of brown and grey swipes of paint, not her usual bright swirls and splashes. I figured she'd been in a hurry to get back to the dress-up corner.

"It's yuk," she said, frowning and throwing it on the floor. I thought she had a very good point but Kev — ever the champion of his girls — talked it up. "It's great, Katie. Beautiful. Good job. Yay for you."

She looked at him with four-year-old scepticism.

"Yay nothing," she said.

That's how I felt now. Yay nothing.

But still I smiled, my jaw tight with tension.

"You seem good. Are you upbeat?" a friend said.

Dumb question. Cancer was squatting in my house. How would I be upbeat?

"Not sure about upbeat," I said. "I'm stable. We're doing what we can."

"Everything will be ok," another friend said.

"Will it?" I volleyed back, knowing my life had taken a radical turn down a dark alley and there was no navigation tool to help me find my way back.

"It'll just be different…and that's ok….change is good," she persisted.

"How is it ok?" I wanted to scream. I liked my other life. The one where my husband could walk over to the fridge and take the milk out without dropping it on the floor.

In my Before Cancer life, I liked change. I embraced it, I enjoyed it, I even chased it, wanting to suck all the learning out of it. But not when it was forced on me and the shadow kept coming even when I was backing away from it. I could cope, I knew I could, but the truth was that this was not what I wanted, I hated my new life — I was scared of it — and I couldn't say the words out loud because everyone was counting on me.

So this is what I did.

- Smiled graciously at everyone who was trying to help, to be there for us.

- Hugged everyone who brought food and did practical things because it really, really helped. It meant I didn't have to do these things when I was trying to do everything else.

- Structured my days as much as possible so I knew what I had to do from the moment I got out of bed.

- Stayed steady for all the people I loved, who were looking to me to lead this crazy expedition for as long as it took, to wherever it was going.

And this is what I felt.

- Grateful to people who wrote thoughtful cards and letters and messages without expecting a reply, admiring of those who picked up the phone even when they didn't know what to say to me or were afraid of saying the wrong thing.

- Indebted to those who did small practical things — dropped in baking that helped to feed all our visitors or meals I could stow in the freezer; mowed our lawn, waterblasted our deck, cleared my junk mail, brought in the rubbish bins — by way of caring.

- Happy that I had a close family and good friends, old and new, who I knew would go the distance for me.

- Hurt by people I counted as good friends, who backed away, even though I understood the fear that cancer ignites in some people: both of the disease and of intruding on our privacy.

- Tired. Emotionally wasted. The life-sucking kind of tired you can't fix with sleep. (If you could sleep.)

The emails and text messages poured in. Wonderful, caring, funny messages from our friends, acquaintances, colleagues. My clients, too, sent messages: police officers, cricket players, athletes and many others shelving their own problems to spare a thought for mine. Electronic media is helpful that way: it's a vehicle for those who don't know you well or who don't want to intrude to offer their love and support. And to give you a laugh. It also provides a shield from the world and space to read and reply to messages at your own pace. It was comforting to know people were thinking of us, of me.

But when close friends communicate with you only by text message it can have a jagged edge. It doesn't carry any emotion; and it requires so little time and effort that you can be left wondering if 30 seconds is all you are worth.

- Hi hrd kevvy sick. Love and thinkin of u.
- OMG Kev in hosp. All thking of u. Let me know what I can do.
- Here w a wine if u need it :-)
- All our love. U in our thoughts and prayers.

I texted people back as quickly as I could, or could handle. Ever polite, an overblown sense of duty, the legacy of being the eldest child and a psychologist: a person who will always DO THE RIGHT THING.

"Thanks for thinking of us," I wrote. "He's home now, doing really well; a glass of wine might be nice sometime."

When what I really wanted to say was "Happy to be in your thoughts and prayers. Now would you mind following up those prayers with a chicken casserole?" or "If you really bloody care bring that bottle of wine over, pour me a glass and sit with me and have a laugh while I find my way through this mess."

I understood why some people stayed away. Cancer is to the body what psychosis is to the mind: it scares the living shit out of people. It flags the possibility that someone might DIE. It makes even some of your good friends frightened to pick up a telephone. When making that contact is the best thing to do — even for yourself.

As my mother used to tell us: "Pick the phone up quickly. Put aside your own fear and make the call, even if you don't know what to say. Show people you care. If you leave it too long, you won't be able to do it. Nor will you ever be able to look them in the eye."

But not everyone has my mother for a teacher.

I tried hard to stay neutral to the reactions of others; I knew that just because cancer had frozen our lives temporarily, other people were tracking on: they had their own turmoil and stresses to deal with.

But it didn't stop me wanting people to say "God this sucks for you, what a nightmare," even though I almost wouldn't let them for fear it would unravel me.

"Can I come visit?" texted a friend.

"Sure, this weekend's good. We'd love to see you," I wrote back. Subscript: hurry up, he might not be here very long.

"Soz, not this weekend." she replied, like I'd pressured her. "The kids have so much on. I'm under the pump."

Was it fear that made her say that? Or could she really not find 20 minutes in her whole weekend?

Or was I too sensitive? I couldn't tell. It's hard to keep perspective when you are operating in a bubble of illness. Shock and worry skew everything. People were trying but, with my world tilted, it felt like they were getting it slightly wrong: not caring enough, too grim, too earnest, too solutions-focused, too soppy, too bright and positive.

It wasn't them, it was me.

The truth was that there were some days when people couldn't provide what I needed because I didn't know myself. All I knew was that for hundreds of people, my clients, I had sat there every day, doing exactly the right thing, working through their emotions, helping them sit with the pain, feel it, adjust to it, then figuring out a way to slowly, gently get through it. And when I found myself standing knee deep in crap, I just wanted someone to do that for me.

But who? God was clearly busy. My family had enough to worry about — I could read the angst on their faces — and I was supposed to be looking after them. I wanted to save my friends to have fun with (when I felt like having fun again). And I didn't feel like paying a psychologist to tell me things I already knew.

"Let's sit down on the couch," I said to myself sternly one afternoon when Kev was napping in the bedroom. "You and I need to have a little chat."

I put some music on — one of the big ballads I danced to when no-one else was at home — poured myself a large glass of wine. Then I hauled out my laminated copy of Elisabeth Kubler Ross's *Five Stages of Grief and Loss*.

Even though I knew loss couldn't be packaged into neat stages, that it was a unique experience to each person, I needed to process all that I was feeling, to normalise my emotions.

"Denial and Isolation. Anger. Bargaining. Depression." I said out loud. "And sadness. Fear. I'm so scared of what's up ahead."

"It's normal to feel like this, all this messed up, mixed up emotion. It is healthy. It's a process. There's no need to rush through it, you don't have to hurry to the other side. Just let it wash through," I said.

"But it's so hard for you," a whiny negative voice whispered in my ear. "He might die. You might be on your own in a few months."

Wait a minute.

From somewhere I recalled being with my sister Lisa one evening — she had to sing to a large after-dinner audience and performance anxiety was chewing her up. She needed psychological help. Using red lipstick I scrawled a really empathetic note on a paper napkin and handed it to her:

"Step the f*** up!"

She had laughed, mouthed "bitch" at me, walked up on the stage and blown everyone away with her performance.

"You're going to be ok," I said to myself. "You know how to play this cancer game. So STEP THE F*** UP AND DO IT."

Suddenly, I felt my mood lift. Crazy times. There I was at home, sitting on the couch, playing music, drinking wine, talking to myself. Loudly.

I took a big sip of wine.

"You absolute freaking weirdo," I said and burst out laughing.

Chapter 8

THE RUMOUR

Tess came home from a party late one night. It was gone midnight when we heard the door open, her heels slap against the wooden floors. She had never been one to sneak in quietly and usually called out "Hey guys, I'm home" no matter what the hour.

But tonight she said nothing, just banged her way through the house. I was awake, as usual, and I found her in the living room, sitting in Kev's armchair. She hadn't turned on the lights.

"They were talking about Kevvo at the party," she said, darkly, yanking her hair out of its high knot. For some reason I noticed her long hair was back its nearly natural brunette again, not the blue or green she'd been favouring most of this year.

"What do you mean?"

"There's a rumour going round. That he's dying."

She'd been at a party with some old school friends. One of them had passed on the word on the streets. I hadn't heard it but I wasn't surprised. Karori was a big suburb — New Zealand's largest — but it was a village when it came to gossip.

I felt my jaw clench. It's not what you want your daughter to hear when she has gone out for the evening to get away from the illness, the unspoken fear, at home.

"People say stuff like that when they're scared," I said, keeping my anger in check.

"Do you think it's true?" Tess looked at me now, brow furrowing, willing me to knock the rumour on the head but threatening to laser me with her eyes if I lied.

I sidestepped. Because I had to.

"It's cancer Tessie. It's not the flu."

Further swerve tactics required. "But you know all those stories dad told you about his marathon running?"

A suspicious look. "Yeah, yeah. Like the one where the lactic acid got him and he had to walk backwards up stairs for days because he was in so much pain."

"What does that tell you about him?

"That he tells long, boring running stories?"

We both smiled.

"He's a tough guy," I said.

"Nooooo. He's such a baby." I knew what she meant.

He was warm and empathetic with his girls, always full of praise and hugs; almost feminine in his style of relating to them. He had always let his words, his behaviour, show them how a good man treats women.

"That baby has also run 11 marathons."

"So?"

"So he knows how to hang in there. He knows hitting the wall doesn't mean it's over."

"Yeah but I don't," she said into the darkness.

Chapter 9

THE BULLY

Our living room had been transformed into what looked like a daycare lounge for the elderly. Sun poured in, Kev dozed in his worn armchair, surrounded by tissues and books and bottles. He was so wobbly on the walking frame, he needed someone to trail behind him as he crashed and clattered over the wooden floors.

"Clatterman," we called him. Clats, for short. He couldn't sneak up on anyone. He couldn't answer the doorbell before callers gave up waiting and left. He couldn't reach the lollies Tess and I stowed just out of his reach.

"Meanies," he whined. He had a serious sweet tooth.

"You can't exercise. You can't even go for a walk. Lollies

will make you fat."

"I've got cancer. I might die. You have to give me whatever I want."

We laughed and left the sweets just out of his grasp.

He couldn't sleep in our bed because there wasn't room to park his walker. He couldn't remember which drugs to take, when. He couldn't shower by himself. He needed help to put on his underpants.

He lost his dignity. I lost my independence.

I was afraid to leave him alone. I did errands quickly. At the local mall, I screeched into the disabled car parking space and slapped Kev's new orange disability permit on the dashboard, ignoring the rule that forbade me from using it unless the disabled person was in the passenger seat.

As I got out of the car into light rain a woman hissed at me.

"You can't park there." She was in her forties. Hands on hips. Scarlet lipstick. Pouting.

Only a metre away from me.

"You're not disabled. YOU NEED TO MOVE," she said.

Genius, I thought. They were dark, sarcastic thoughts, even though I knew she was right and I was wrong — I was officially breaking the Rules of Disability Parking. But I had never cared much for rules and I cared even less now.

"People like you are a disgrace," she said.

I felt the movie reel of the past three weeks start to spin. Back to when my able bodied husband had bounded out the door to work. Back to when I had rushed out behind him. Now he sat all day in an armchair with withered legs, medication-induced constipation and uncontrollable hiccups. His back was so weakened with cancer and radiation that a stumble could shatter his spine. A fall would kill him more quickly than cancer.

That's why I had to shop fast.

The tangle of my emotions — fear, sadness, rage — had risen to the surface, tiny bubbles in a pot of water as it begins to boil.

This woman didn't know me, didn't know my life. She just took aim, her weapon loaded with judgment, because I hadn't staggered out of the car.

I stared at her, pressing my lips together tightly so the ugliness couldn't escape. She glared back at me as the rain dusted our hair.

An image from many years earlier slid into my mind. I was nine years old. I had beaten up a boy who had bullied my little brother and then stolen his football. OUR football. The boy, a pale redhead, was taller and bigger than us. Fatter and softer, too.

"Let's get him," I hissed, under my breath.

We flew at him, wrapping our arms around his legs, staying low, letting the momentum of our bodies take him down. Our father had taught us well: he came from an era when women were secretaries, teachers and nurses until they became mothers — but he had no sexist biases when it came to rugby. Girls had the same rights as boys when it came to learning how to tackle. It was an essential life skill.

"Little guys can take down big guys if they do it right," he coached his two eager pupils in the back yard. "It's about technique, not size."

I got my brother to hold the boy's feet then I had punched him over and over until his nose spouted blood, until he screamed. He shook his head, the blood sprayed up in the air, and we let go. Frightened, but triumphant, we grabbed the football and ran off.

"It's a secret," I told Rhys who, at seven, did everything I said. "Mum and dad might get mad. And we won't go back to the park or he might bring his friends to get us. Smash us to bits."

Rhys stared at me wide-eyed, fearful, but nodding his head.

We never mentioned it again but for days, weeks, the arc of the boy's blood, the scream stayed with me. I had scared myself with the force inside me, with the explosion of it. Even now, when my angriest clients describe the red mist coming down I know, can remember, what they mean.

And, now, I felt it again.

Do people sense fury? Or can they just see it? In the carpark, the woman with the red lipstick kept her eyes on my face as she backed away. I stood there, in the drizzling rain, blinking until the mist settled and I could focus my eyes. I took several deep breaths, counting slowly to ten.

I watched her get into her car.

When I took my hands out of my coat pockets, they were balled into fists.

Fifteen minutes later, I was standing in the supermarket queue when my cellphone rang. I checked the number: unidentified. I'd been letting these calls go to voicemail because I didn't feel like talking about cancer with people I didn't know well — nor did I want any new clients just now.

But for some reason, on this day, perhaps because the woman in the carpark had jigged with my equilibrium, I hit the answer button.

"Karen?" a tentative woman's voice said and, when I confirmed, a heard a quick breath, a stifled sob.

It was the mother of a client I hadn't seen for more than a year, a young footballer with an off-season cannabis habit, which he had for several years timed carefully to fool the drug testers. He'd seemingly brought the dope under control, along with his accompanying depression and anxiety, and I'd discharged him.

"It's Sam," his mum said. Breathless, edgy.

"He's at home, pacing the house, ranting, saying strange things, I didn't know what to do, who to call."

"It's ok," I heard myself say, surprised at the evenness in my voice and even more surprised at what I said next because I was supposed to be shopping at speed to get home to my armchair-bound husband.

"What's your address?" I asked, recalling they lived just one suburb over from mine. "I'll come over."

I didn't usually do house calls. Psychologists working in private practice see people in their offices or chambers. House calls are not an economic use of time; and more importantly, when you don't have the back-up of a community mental health team on tap, it's not safe.

So I was not sure why I offered to do this.

Perhaps I just wanted to stop being a cancer nurse for a few minutes and step back into a world that felt so familiar to me, one I was not scared of because I knew what to do. Perhaps I knew desperation when I heard it in a parent's voice, perhaps I just wanted to think about someone other than myself and my cancer-stricken life for a while.

I raced home and dropped off the groceries.

"I'm going out for a bit," I told Kev who was parked up in the chair he had spent the past eight hours in, apart from a handful of snail-paced journeys to the bathroom. Our old dog Tommy, a Shih Tzu, lay across his knee, snoring. He and Kev had taken to spending a lot of time together. I was pleased: Tommy, with his unconditional love of food and our family (in that order) was good therapy.

"Sure," he replied, stroking Tom's long soft fur. "Take your time. I'm not going anywhere."

When I pulled up at Sam's address I heard a ball bouncing on concrete. I followed the sound down a broken path around the back of the house and there he was: bouncing a dull orange basketball under a homemade hoop, walking in circles, raving about some people, some things, who were coming after him. His blonde hair was plastered down with sweat, even though he was only wearing a singlet and it was a grey, chilly day. The rain had stopped, but it was still threatening overhead.

"Hey Sam."

"They're over there," he said, eyeing me, his eyes rolling back in his head. "In the bushes. Look out!" He flung the basketball at my head. I ducked sideways and it smashed into the side of the house.

"I need to clean my room," he said, frantic, scanning the bushes around us.

"There's dust. So much dust. Who are they? There's something happening. They're planning it. I don't know what. WHO ARE THEY? WHO?

"GET THOSE BASTARDS AWAY FROM ME."

I tossed the ball back to him and sat down on a chipped garden seat, waiting. I knew Sam really well; we worked together for more than two years. He was a brilliant age-group striker, until a drunken car crash rocked his world. Sam was in the back seat of the car, he was thrown clear, with only bruising and a sprained ankle. His mate, the driver, died at the scene. So did their friend in the passenger seat.

The weed Sam smoked to cope had gradually tightened its grip.

I'd seen him suicidal and coiled up with anxiety before but not — never — like this, wild-eyed and insensible. I suspect he'd been smoking again and it had blown him out mentally. He was having a psychotic break. Delusional beliefs. Paranoia. Loss of function. Undoubtedly voices in his head. Command hallucinations: dangerous, because they could order him to do something really dark, from which there would be no comeback.

"Who are you?" he suddenly glared at me, guarded.

"WHO ARE YOU? GET AWAY FROM ME." He held

onto his ball and backed up against the house.

I looked up and saw Sam's mother inside the house, watching us through a small window. We met once a couple of years earlier and we'd spoken on the phone a number of times. Sam's father left her when she was pregnant. She had raised him on her own. She gave a half wave.

Sam bounced the ball faster, muttering, ranting. His body jerked as he moved, he was an athlete but there was no fluidity in his movement right now. Then, without warning, his body sagged, the fight left him, he stood under the hoop, the ball under his arm with his shoelaces untied. He must be 23 by now. A little boy in a man's body.

I stood up and took a couple of steps towards him.

"My turn," I said. His cloudy eyes struggled to focus but I saw a flash of recognition. The ball dropped to the ground. I took a shot and it bounced off the hoop. He rebounded and passed it back to me. I took several more poorly directed shots until he stole the ball and showed me how it was done: fluid now, a soft arc from his right hand. Nothing but net.

"Shot Sam," I said and the corner of his mouth cracked upwards. Not really a smile but enough. "You're not well. Let's keep you safe from those guys," I waved my hand at the bushes.

"What do you reckon we take a ride to the hospital?"

When I got home, I told Kev where I'd been, leaving out the names. I told him the boy was in the lock-up unit at the hospital's psychiatric ward, where he'd be calmed with a cocktail of anti-psychotic and mood-stablising medication.

Kev nodded, he understood.

"Poor kid," he said. Then added: "His poor mother. She'll be out of her mind."

I nodded, appreciating his ability to empathise with someone else when his own mortality was on the line. He was right, though. Worry about your kids outstrips everything. Our situation could be worse.

We sat in silence for a few minutes, then his voice cut in: "It's better that I got cancer than the girls. I couldn't bear that."

I thought about Sam and his mother and the long haul she faced to get her bright, talented son back. I thought of the parents I'd seen as clients who had lost their children in accidents or suicides, I imagined what I would be feeling if either of our daughters was sitting in Kev's seat right now, pale, nauseous and in the grip of serious illness.

I opened my mouth to speak but then closed it again. It didn't seem right to say it, even though it was true: I'd rather lose my husband than my kids.

"Know yourself."

Dr Seuss

Chapter 10

THE BODY REMEMBERS

When cancer rears up in front of you, you use everything — everything — in your personal bag of tricks to counter it.

If I'd been a nutritionist, I'd have bought a juicer and eliminated red meat from our diet. If I'd been a yoga master we'd have been sitting cross-legged on the floor at dawn, emptying our minds. But I was a psychologist: a talk therapist. So if Kev wasn't keen on laying bare his emotions and feelings, he wasn't going to get away with it.

I wanted to do my bit. I had to do everything I could to give him the best chance of recovery. I didn't want him to get less than I would give to my clients; I wanted him to have more.

The trouble was, how do you get a man who has always lightly scorned the mountain of self-help books on my side of the bed to address old emotional wounds? To examine his belief systems? To think about how he deals with stress?

How do you do therapy with your husband?

I knew what not to do. Sit him on my couch and ask him how he was feeling. That would have distressed him more than rampaging cancer cells. He was a talker, a joker and a storyteller but he was not inclined to explore his own emotions. So I needed a sly approach. Hit a man when he's down.

I sat down on the floor next to him one morning while he did his prescribed exercises, trying to raise his withered legs a couple of centimetres off the ground.

"Why do you think you got cancer?" I said, waiting for the brush off.

It didn't come. He was too busy grunting with muscular effort.

We'd already been through this. Everyone who gets felled by serious illness asks "why me?" It's a natural part of trying to make sense of it. In his first week in hospital Kev made a half-hearted protest about the unfairness of it all: "I thought if I was a good person, worked hard, provided for my family, didn't cheat on my wife I'd escape cancer or any other big nasty. There are prisons full of arseholes. Why me and not them?"

But he didn't dwell on it. A committed newsman, he was fond of saying he dealt in facts, not fiction. And definitely not feelings.

Science over art. Certainty over possibility.

His approach to cancer was the same: solutions over questions. Pain over pity. Chemo over God.

"You already know what I think," he said, struggling against the weight of his legs. He was desperate to be able to stand up unaided so he could start putting golf balls along the carpet. A marathon man's philosophy: do a little bit every day. Small steps. Big results.

And I did know.

In his mind, Kev had written his cancer script. He'd probably had a stomach ulcer lurking around for years. Then he got an infection and his immune system got all screwed up trying to combat it.

"The cells went haywire on me. Just damn unlucky," he said.

I had my theory too, and I wasn't sure he would buy it. I knew he'd be sceptical of the idea that cancer, like all physical illness, was the body's alarm system going off, a plea to silence the internal chaos, a call for psychological and lifestyle change.

I knew he'd take up every physical and medical treatment on offer, that he'd do everything for his body that the doctors' ordered, while anything to do with his head and heart would be up for debate.

But I had him on the rack. Especially when he could see a golf club standing in the corner of the room. I left it there on purpose. A way forward. A visual symbol of Hope.

The truth is no-one knows what causes cancer. Plenty of people, qualified and otherwise, think they do but cancer has eluded them all. More than 100 possible causes have been floated, but none pinned down.

Kev and I had been through just some of the possibilities, trying to make some sense of it. In one of our lighter moments we had brainstormed it, checking off the potential culprits, one by one.

- Insecticides and toxic sprays

- Burnt barbecue meat

- (Too much) Coffee

- Radiation exposure

- Pharmaceuticals

- Cell phones

- Wood dust

- Lead based paint

- Asbestos

- Sunbeds

- Unidentified virus

- Smoking

- Obesity

- Shift work

"Could have been the paint," Kev said. "I stripped a house of paint once. I wasn't wearing a mask and it could have been lead based. Or wood dust. I've done a lot of DIY in my time." Neither of us wanted to finger coffee.

"You did shift work too."

"I've had a cell phone forever."

"And you do love a burnt sausage."

He looked at me, deadpan as ever.

"You're right. I was a sitter."

We laughed but the question hung there.

Why? Why? Why? There wasn't even a family history to throw arrows at. We were lost. Just like so many others.

But I knew there was one way to frame cancer's unexpected knock on our door so it made sense to the journalist in him: as a story.

Like every illness, mental or physical, cancer weaves a tale unique to the person who is hosting it. Our biology combines with our environment and experiences to set up patterns in how we think and behave. When events compromise these patterns, it triggers responses in the mind and/or body which can lead to dysfunction or illness.

The first step in treating any illness in a person is to figure out his or her story, the combination of biology, environment, history and lifestyle factors that have led to this place. In clinical psychology, this process is called a formulation.

But, really, it's just a story.

Cancer, I believed, was not solely a physical disease. It had an emotional core which could often be tracked to human trauma or, more accurately, loss: a death or the ending of a significant relationship or even a lost opportunity, such as the experience of being a parent through infertility, termination, miscarriage or the death of a child.

The body holds onto this old hurt.

The body remembers.

Over time, this trauma can create internal chaos, confusing the body's systemic function and making it vulnerable to disease. Many people probably live for years in this state, without ever knowing it, without crossing into serious illness territory. It takes something in the environment — from contact with toxins to exposure to emotional stress — to trigger the frenzied cellular response that is the hallmark of cancer.

It's a theory with ancient roots.

I first came across the mind-body connection as a 17-year-old in a history of physical education lecture. I thought it was the smartest thing I'd ever heard but my lecturer, Dr Rex Thomson, was simply relaying the ideas first touted by the Greek philosophers: that the body is a reflection of emotional state (thoughts and feelings) and lifestyle, that it is not possible to split one off from the other, that both must work in harmony to achieve healthy function.

Many since then have offered an emotional explanation to an array of ailments and illness, which has spawned an industry in its own right.

I've spent years studying this connection and done emotional work with many people suffering from pain and various physical illnesses. Sometimes they have blanked, or plastered over, the trauma in their lives; sometimes they have forgotten and don't even know it's there. Sometimes they think staring it down, opening the wound, will cause a bleed that they won't be able to stop.

But as a psychologist, I believe digging for, and finding some peace, with your emotional wounds is an essential part of recovery. It may not be so much about addressing loss but recognizing that how you operated previously is not the way you need to do things now. Sometimes people still react in the same way they did as children, hurt, bewildered and frightened. It's just not as easy to recognize when the hurt child has greying hair and wrinkles.

Most importantly, though, your psychology, like your lifestyle, is one piece of the cancer puzzle that you can do something about.

That's what I wanted for Kev. Perhaps selfishly, I was determined to help him. So as he lay there, helpless, I opened the file.

"Colleen," I said. "Let's talk about her."

Colleen was Kev's elder sister, lost to the family through medical error when he was just three years old.

"I've told you the story," he said. But he didn't look defensive; just tired and vulnerable.

He'd told me how his parents, armed with a new teddy bear, had gone to the hospital to collect their six-year-old daughter after a routine appendix removal. They'd been stopped in the corridor and told their little girl wouldn't be going home with them. She'd flown through the operation but died in recovery when some shoddy suturing burst open.

His mother had vomited on the floor.

The autopsy later showed she had not even had an inflamed appendix.

Over the years I'd added my own thoughts about what happened. How his parents, crippled with grief, would have been stripped of their capacity to help their son who did not understand death, only that his sister was gone. His father spent longer hours on the farm; his mother struggled with a new baby who wouldn't feed. So the toddler buried his loss, deep in his soul, while the ghoulish Moonhawk birds invaded his dreams.

There was more too.

Kev's parents separated when he was 13, supporting statistics which show the death of a child is one of the leading causes of marriage breakdown, possibly as high as 80-90 percent.

But who really knows?

He was in his first year at boarding school when it happened, homesick and struggling with the bullying hierarchy of an all male environment. The split was unexpected: he'd never heard his parents argue. Kev found out when his dad was hours late to pick him up for the school holidays and, when he finally turned up, his mother and little sister were not there. Kev's younger brother filled him in when his dad got out at a petrol station to refuel the car.

"Mum's gone," Philip said. "So's Carolyn." Just facts. No explanations. Just a home life that was split in two: mum's house, dad's house. Where to go for Christmas.

Loss, upon loss.

For the second time in his life he tucked his feelings deep inside while he got on with the emotional challenges of the teenage years.

Now, he lay on the floor, struggling to roll over, having to lift his useless legs by hand. His face was pale with exertion.

"What was Colleen like…what do you remember?"

I felt guilty for pressing it, especially on someone who couldn't move. I expected him to shut down on me, maybe snap in frustration.

But he stopped wrestling with his legs and stared at the ceiling.

"I remember Vets and Cows."

I waited.

"She was always the cow." He smiled.

"When she died the house went quiet. I guess everyone was heartbroken. I didn't understand it but I could feel it. Just the silence."

"Did you miss her growing up?"

He shrugged. "It was what I knew. You get on with things. I had Cool Phil and Carolyn. But I've often thought about what it would have been like to have a big sister. She'd be in her fifties now. I wonder what sort of woman she'd have been. "

"She may well be sitting right here, visiting you."

I saw him swallow.

A change of tack. A leading question. But I was allowed to. This was the lounge floor, not a courtroom.

"Did you get sick much when you were a kid?"

Pause.

"I had a lot of time off school with stomach aches and things. Whenever I got nervous I would make myself vomit. I could actually bring it on by thinking about it. It got me out of doing things I didn't want to do.

"Good party trick."

He looked thoughtful. "But then it sort of became real. My stomach started to get really dodgy with food. Still is. You know I can't eat cream, can't do fish and chips and beer."

It was true. Rich or spicy food messed with his digestion and led to hours in the bathroom. Especially if it was mixed with alcohol.

"Do you reckon you might have always stored your stress in your stomach? That it might have started way back, like when you were three?

He frowned.

"Mum said I always had stomach aches."

"Could that be why the cancer first set up in your stomach? I mean why did you get it there — and not somewhere else — your lungs, your liver, your bowel? That it went after your stomach because that was your weak spot from when you were a kid?"

Now he looked over at me, nodding slowly. In that moment I knew I had the most unlikely of converts to therapy.

"It makes sense," he said.

The cow and her vet: Colleen Norquay was the cow, little brother Kevin the vet who in the end couldn't save her, 1959.

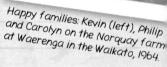

Happy families: Kevin (left), Philip and Carolyn on the Norquay farm at Waerenga in the Waikato, 1964.

Marathon man: In full flight for Wellington Harriers. Who knew then that running would teach him how to cope with cancer? 1981.

The 70s: Kev on vocals as Molehill rock it out at his 21st. Vern Wood on bass, Ian Purdie the guitarist. Hamilton, January 1976.

A special day: out go the wedding invites, with an appropriately journalistic theme. The big day was December 6, 1991.

Kate and Tess after raiding Dorothy Fitzpatrick's dress-up box, Blenheim, 1996.

THE DOMINION

FRIDAY DECEMBER 6, 1991

Journos to tie the knot

P.M. "no comment" on invite snub

The Fletcher Marathon
Great cause or great contract?

Mr Horomia, a word please: pursuing the new Maori Affairs Minister, Parliament 1999.

BGW committee: Kevin Kane (left) and Tim Richards were right there for us when things went off the fairway, Martinborough, December 2011.

Not what we had in mind: Tess (far right) celebrated her 18th birthday, in Wellington Hospital, July 2012.

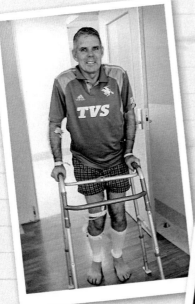

No more a runner: trying a new form of transport, Wellington Hospital, July 2012.

New hairstyle, August, 2012.

Golf as therapy: out of the rough, back on the fairway.

So far, so good: celebrating at Tim and Kamala's wedding, Port Hills, February 2014.

A quiet night in: a typical family gathering, Karori, 2014

Chapter 11

THE BUS MONSTER

A Bedtime Story, by Kevin Norquay

It is early evening and the girls, aged six and four, have had a bath and are dressed for bed. Wet combed hair, checked summer pyjamas, pink and blue, clambering around their father for a bedtime story.

"Tell us the Bus Monster." Kate says. Always the spokesperson.

"Again?" Kev drops his work satchel and sinks onto the sofa.

"Yeeeeesssss," they trill. "It's our favourite."

The Bus Monster is the current pick of the many stories Kev has made up for the girls since they could sit on his knee. They prefer these tales to books mostly, I think, because they always have a starring role.

Broken down, there is only ever one theme to these stories: the kids always emerge as heroes.

Small over big. Brains over brawn. Good over evil.

Justice always wins through.

The Bus Monster comes in various versions depending on how tired Kev is that night. But the central character was a huge creature, with a thrashing head and savage teeth who hides in tunnels waiting for school buses to drive through.

"What's his favourite snack?" Kev asks.

"CHILDREN," they yell.

"That's right. He loves school buses because he can chomp 30 children at a time. RAAAAAARRRRRRR."

The girls scream.

"And who saves these children?

"Kate and Tess," they chant, giggling.

"Kate and Tess are clever. They have an utterly brilliant idea," he makes it sound as if it is the first time he's ever told the story.

"They cover the bus in hot chilli sauce. It drives through the tunnel and the monster opens his ugly stinky mouth and chomps. His mouth explodes in flames as the fire burns him up.

"He screams and SCREAMS!

"And that's the end of the Bus Monster."

The girls beam.

Then he adds the life lesson.

"If you are smart you can do anything, overcome all the bad stuff in the world. You just have to use your brains.

"You just need a clever plan."

"Do you remember the Bus Monster?" Kev said.

It was the morning of his first chemotherapy session and we were on our way to the hospital. I was driving because his legs weren't yet reliable enough on the brakes; he was talking. Of course I remembered the Bus Monster. Although I hadn't heard the story for about 10 years, it was etched into our family folklore.

"You know what I'm thinking? That cancer is our Bus Monster."

He didn't need to say any more than that. I got it.

"Bigger than us. Darker. Sharper teeth. Watching us. Waiting to pounce and chew us up," he said.

"Well," I said, thinking. "In that story the little guy always wins."

He chuckled.

"Are you scared?" I asked.

"Of chemo? Not really. I want to get the treatment started. At least we'll be doing something."

It wasn't what I meant. I meant was he scared of dying. But I gripped the steering wheel and focused on the road.

The Bus Monster was fiction. In real life I knew the bad guy didn't always go up in flames. I knew justice wasn't always done, that cancer had claimed an awful lot of good people.

There was no point in going head to head with the Cancer Monster. We would lose. We needed to play smart, we needed a clever plan.

"We need to write our own story, a new one," I said.

Kev nodded. "Luckily, stories are what we're good at."

The first line was written for us when we arrived at the cancer day ward. Yellow balloons floating around the reception desk, a whiteboard covered in smiley faces, rainbows and hand-drawn daffodils.

"Welcome to Fun Friday," scrawled across the board. "What a great day outside! The sun is shining! Hello all you beautiful people."

We found a seat in the wait room and looked at each other. Seriously? We knew whoever wrote those words was trying to lift spirits of cancer patients but they jarred against the reason we were all gathered here.

The people in the wait room either had a potentially fatal disease or were worried out of their minds for someone they loved. We were all waiting. Waiting. Waiting for test results, words that could change lives, or to be injected with drugs so potent they could strip paint.

"Fun, Funsie Friday? Kev said, his journalistic cynicism surfacing. "I can think of another F word they could have used to go with Friday. And with cancer for that matter."

We laughed, quietly, but it was still enough to rip through the silence and heaviness of the wait room. The other people lined up on either side of the room looked over at us. I felt a start of guilt for having fun in a cancer clinic. But I didn't care either — you have to get through any way you can.

And Kev was on a roll.

"They need a new weather forecaster too. Can't they see it's raining out there?"

Chapter 12

WHITE ROSES

Cancer treatment comes in three forms, medically speaking, and it is served up in a raft of combinations.

Surgery. Radiation. Chemotherapy.

Cut. Burn. Poison.

There is the "watch and wait" approach too which could also be called crossing your fingers, upping your vegetable intake, and hoping for the best.

But we were way past that. With surgery ruled out and radiation therapy completed, we were in the third arena. Chemical warfare.

Chemotherapy is as it sounds: the administering of highly toxic, eye-wateringly expensive chemicals into the body with the aim of blasting often fast-growing cancer cells into submission. Stopping their march. Killing them. It is accepted, also, that these medicines will poison healthy cells and stymie normal physical function too. But when mutating rogue blood cells are galloping through your lymphatic system it seems to be inviting trouble to say no to it.

Kev was all over it, pumping to get treatment underway. I was too, even though it ran contrary to my belief in the body to heal itself naturally, given time and a little prompting. This cancer, we've been told, was just too far gone.

"Shouldn't we explore alternative treatments too?" I had asked when he first got home. It was my lame attempt at a holistic approach.

"No," Kev had said bluntly. "I've already given up sausages."

We had laughed at that and I'd let it go, knowing that one of the keys to recovery is to believe in the treatment. Kev had to believe; I needed to be fully on board too.

Now, as the nurse dug at his arm to find a vein, the laughing had stopped. It was business time.

Chemotherapy drugs come in a dazzling array of types and doses and combinations; they can be administered orally through tablets or intravenously via a drip. Kev's drugs were called RCHOP and they flowed into him through a plastic bag hanging from a portable IV machine. It bleeped every time the bag emptied and the chemo nurses scurried to replace it. They wore shapeless purple gowns over their uniforms because the drugs were so toxic that a single misplaced drop would sear fabric, if not skin.

Over breakfast we'd run through our strategy for the day. Kev had agreed to use imagery, a sports psychology technique that stops your mind from straying into negative places and allows you to mentally manipulate high pressure situations.

I wanted him to think of chemotherapy as a gentle process, promoting the growth of healthy cells, rather than an aggressive killing off bad ones.

"When the drugs are going in, picture your body filling up with white light….gently melting away the tumours."

He had looked at me as though I was delusional.

Dumb idea. Too soppy. New tactic needed. "The best athletes all use imagery. It will improve your golf."

"Really?" he had said, brightly. Bingo.

Now, as the bag dripped, he leant back on the pillow, closed his eyes and murmured "white roses, white roses."

Then he opened one eye. He was winding me up.

"You promised. And it's white light, not bloody roses."

He smiled. "Ok, I'll do it. I'm not exactly on the front foot here."

He settled in for the six-hour session, growing paler and more heavy-lidded as the clock ticked. I opened my book. Cancer pro: time to read, even though my concentration was shot.

"Hey Norks," a voice cut through the chemo-heavy air.

A man in a navy woollen beanie sauntered over. A woman of about my age followed him, smiling. It was

Nigel Llewellyn, an old Waikato University friend of Kev's who he used to catch up with for a beer every few months. That had ceased about a year earlier when Nigel got sick. A livid purple scar was visible where his hat met his scalp, evidence of brain tumour surgery.

We made introductions, chatted a while, and Nigel said he was on the way back. A new drug, he said. It had taken aim at the tumour in his brain, it had even begun to shrink. His voice was full of hope.

I wasn't sure what to think. I'd heard Nigel was terminally ill with only a few months left. His face was taupe, gaunt. His clothes flapped around him like washing on a clothesline. His partner was attractive, thin, tired looking. They were chemo — cancer — veterans. I didn't like the look of that experience.

While Nigel chatted to Kev, his partner and I eyed each other uneasily. What to say? Small talk didn't feel quite right. She didn't say anything and I was grateful because I didn't have to respond. I knew she knew where I was headed, she'd been there, was still there — but way ahead of me.

We stood there awkwardly in the ward. She unsure how to coach the rookie who was stepping into a whole new way of life. Me unsure what to say to the veteran whose career was in the twilight zone.

I could read the emotion she was feeding me through her eyes and it made my stomach clench.

Not sadness. Not fear. No, It was something far more threatening to my mental resolve: it was pity.

It's the fallout of chemo that's the bitch.

The bone grinding fatigue, the sickly pallor, the nausea and retching; the constant threat of fevers and infection because even the healthy white blood cells have been blasted into submission.

Then there's the dizziness, the muscle wasting and/or bloating, the dry mouth and ulcers, the constipation, the hair loss, strands at first then handfuls, and finally clumps in the shower, jamming the plug hole, creepy to touch.

Some people gain weight; others shrink at a frightening pace.

Kev lost 16kg in three weeks, most of it from legs stripped of muscle because he couldn't use them. His normal enthusiasm for food disappeared, his diet hung on the only foods he could tolerate: ice blocks, barley sugars and ginger beer.

As his body contracted, his face blew up. Puffy and gaunt at the same time. His teeth seemed to protrude, or maybe his mouth had sagged. His stomach was bruised from anti-blood clot injections, bloated with drugs and inactivity. Bald and shrunken, he was unrecognisable from a month earlier when he'd first entered hospital.

One morning, wearing just a pair of jockey underpants, he staggered into the bathroom. I tried to hide my shock, horror, at the change in his physical form.

"You look like Gandhi," I said, picturing the famed

Indian leader shortly before his assassination: reed thin and bald; hunched and hobbling down the road in his loin cloth.

I was trying to make light of things but my words fell flat. I stopped myself from finishing the sentence:

"No disrespect to Gandhi but I never wanted to sleep with him."

You have to hold onto the knowledge that it is the chemotherapy — the treatment — that makes a person with cancer look so sick. While it's comforting to know that, it is not always easy to remember.

A few years earlier a younger friend of mine was diagnosed with ovarian cancer. She was only 32. It was my first view of cancer up close and she asked me to help her choose a wig. Uneasy with my feelings, with how, and how much, of them to show, I swooped on the chance to do something practical for her. She was an alternative, colourful person and she went from blonde strands to red spikes in a heartbeat, embracing the physical change like it was a stroke of luck.

I went with her to *Look Good, Feel Better*, a sponsored programme where women with cancer are given free makeup and shown how to apply it, how to frame faces without eyebrows, heads without hair.

The room was quiet as the women removed wigs and head scarves, revealing bald and tufted heads, their naked selves. I tried to focus on the generous pile of make up in front of my friend so no-one would feel I was staring at them.

"Wow, so much free stuff," she said.

It was true, the products were fantastic, but I squashed my envy. It didn't seem the right forum to be jealous.

People murmured awkwardly as they tested the products. But as the morning progressed the room filled with an excited buzz. "I wish I'd known how to apply makeup properly before. All those years when I could have been stunning," one woman said, hooting with laughter.

The application of makeup — and the improvement in their physical appearance — gave the women such a psychological lift. You could see it in their eyes, hear it in their voices. And, when they left for the day, you could feel a crackle of fresh energy; for some, hope.

For men, though, there was no such programme.

Perhaps it's because men don't — generally — wear makeup so they were not going to form a queue for a morning of pampering. Nor were men such a good marketing vehicle for the make up companies.

There's an unspoken assumption that men will cope better with the savaging of their looks because they are not as vain as women; that their appearance matters less, that because many men lose their hair anyway a little temporary baldness won't hurt.

It's a big assumption. A man's physical appearance is central to his masculinity and sexuality. When it changes — for the worse — it wounds his confidence and belief in himself as a man.

Kev leaned on a crutch in front of the full-length bedroom mirror. Complementing his underpants was a red and white striped beanie. This was a day after a doctor at the hospital had mistaken me for his daughter; his mother for his sister.

"Shit," he said.

"I'm disgusting. How can you even look at me?"

I knew I should put my arms around him but in that moment I couldn't, or didn't want to. Kev had always been broad in the shoulders and chest, much wider than me. The dark curly mat of hair on his chest had flaked out, leaving him looking sunken and pink. It would have been like hugging a bird. A tiny toxic bird that smelled of metal and ginger beer.

We just looked at each other. His disgust. My guilt.

Cancer.

Chapter 13

THE ENTHUSIASM GAME

They say the clues to your character, to your destiny are laid down in the first decade of your life.

When I was about eight years old my father came home all pumped up from a *Dale Carnegie* motivational seminar. Dale Carnegie was one of the original self-help gurus of the modern era and my dad's love of his work meant I grew up knowing more about him than I ever did about any New Zealand Prime Minister.

So my brother, sister and I sat at his feet and he taught us *"The Enthusiasm Game"*. It was a chant about some jungle animals that was the sort of 70s self-help equivalent of rap. You chanted the rhyme and did crazy moves with your hands and feet at the same time.

"Act enthusiastic and you'll be enthusiastic," we'd shout the punch line.

After a few rounds Rhys and Lisa were bored and ran off to play Cowboys and Horses but I made my dad play it with me every night for weeks. Looking back, it was my first lesson in human psychology. That your thinking creates your reality. Fake it till you make it. Change your thinking and you'll change your life.

But back then I didn't understand all that. All I knew is that *The Enthusiasm Game* made so much more sense to me than Snow White or Goldilocks ever did.

I parked that early lesson up and got on with the business of living. But the intrigue stayed with me and, from the age of about 15, I began to read books, seeking the secret of how to live well, of how to be happy. Not consciously at first. But it was just something that kept drawing me in. Even when I lost my focus in my 20s and drifted through multiple jobs it seemed to me that the most important thing was to live a full, wide life, to squeeze every last drop of juice from it.

Successful living, I called it. I researched and studied ancient Greek philosophers, religion, early self-help gurus, anything I could find on related topics. It was my drug of choice.

And then I met a man who seemed to know all the answers naturally: he was kind to people, he was grateful for everything that came his way, he stayed rooted to the present moment, he eked joy out of the smallest of things.

He had never read a self improvement, or even management, book; he had never set a goal other than how fast he could run a marathon, how much money he could make at the races or how sweetly he could get around a golf course.

When I plotted my goals annually and asked what his were, he'd laugh and say "this year I'm going to paint the letterbox AND fix the leak in the toilet." Then he'd knock off those goals in the first week of the year so that he didn't have to keep thinking about them.

I was curious: I wondered how he had learned the secret of happiness without any conscious search.

And then, seven years after we were married, I figured it out.

Kev went on a journalistic assignment to Papua New Guinea. The 1998 earthquake near the north coast region of PNG caused a tsunami to hit the coast, killing more than 2200 people. It washed bodies up on the beach, wrecked villages and destroyed homes, incomes and lives. He was there to write stories, to pick his way through human bones and carcasses, to record the carnage, the turmoil and the loss.

When he got home he was, like everyone who'd been on the trip, sent to a counsellor for trauma therapy, a checkup to make sure he was mentally fit to return to work.

The counsellor signed him off, with a slight shake of her head.

"You have a very unusual take on life," she said.

He had told her that when he left home in the morning he never expected he would return home to find everything the same.

"People — my family — could have died, gone away, everything could have changed. I don't look forward. I just think about what I have right here, right now and I'm grateful for that," he told her.

You're a fatalist," she said.

"No," Kev said. "I just like to keep it real."

But finally I had my answer to why he was so happy. It was a way of coping. Twice in his life — his sister's death, his parents split — everything he knew had changed in the space of a day, he had not seen utter turmoil coming. Come evening, he didn't trust things to be the same as they were in the morning.

So he kept his expectations minimal. He didn't look ahead or plan for the future. He had a low set point for happiness. Outwardly he was thrilled with the luck life had thrown at him — marriage, kids and a career; inwardly, he expected the worst to happen and armed himself for it emotionally.

So this is what I believe and what I've never told him. That when cancer came calling, in some private mental compartment, he was ready.

Chapter 14

THE HAZARD

It's a hot summer's day in 2003 and we're crammed into our air-conditioning-free car heading out for the evening. It's a family barbecue, over at our friends' home. Kev and I love these people, but our kids and the hosts' children would probably rather be at opposite ends of the globe than spend the next six hours together.

"Can we watch a movie at least?" Kate says from the back seat.

"Or do we have to talk to them all the time."

She's 12, the age when friends begin to trump parents in the weekend entertainment stakes. Her friends were going to the pool that afternoon, then a couple of them were having a *sleepover. There's no question over where she'd rather be.*

I feel guilty. My parents had done the same thing to me. They'd want me to play with, get on with — and even holiday with — a series of kids I often couldn't stand. Kids that, looking back, probably couldn't stand me.

But you realise, with age, that parents need lives too. So now, we are all going to this event. HAPPILY.

As we approach our friends' house I prepare to start up the lecture. I've done it so many times, in so many ways. I hate teaching my kids manners; it reminds me of toddler toilet training, which I also despised and demonstrated very little talent for.

Anticipating trouble. Reminders. Corrections. Praise.

Repeat. Repeat. Repeat.

Say hello. Use names. Look at people. Say please. Say thank you. SHARE.

And then the social nuances that are much harder to teach your children: how to demonstrate the appropriate amount of positive emotion in front of others. Joy. Enthusiasm. Gratitude. And how to publicly temper disappointment, being beaten, anger, envy.

How to be acceptable in the world.

A mixed message. Be yourself. BUT fit in. Be who you are BUT don't be a freak. Most of all, don't embarrass ME.

Arghhhhh. Growing up is hard. Helping your children to grow up to be less screwed up than you are is even harder.

The car is stiflingly hot. I hear my own voice from past lectures in my head. Droning. Nagging. Suddenly, I've had enough of doing this, I've had enough of myself. I cut to the chase and offer up a line, which in time will become part of our family folklore.

"Guys. I'm not going to lecture you. Just......don't act like dead people."

There's silence in the back seat.

Then I hear them laugh.

Death has its own smell. Sort of a rubbery menthol odour, sweet and pungent at the same time, the washout of toxins released through the breath and pores as the body shuts down.

You can smell it in the room when a person is on the way out. But what about a whole floor? Wellington Hospital Ward 5 North, (oncology), had that smell. Or was I just imagining it because it was *the cancer ward*. Most of the patients there were in the end zone, either desperately unwell or preparing to transfer to Hospice care.

The communal lounge was filled with people in pale green hospital gowns dragging IV machines, and their visitors, behind them. A flat screen television blared over conversation. There was always a cake. Where there is sickness, especially pending death, people bring cakes. Or muffins.

"Muffins are the kiss of death," a client with a terminal diagnosis once told me.

"When you're sick everyone brings muffins. There's a muffin for every occasion. Like pick the muffin to match the person. I wonder what the Melanoma Muffin is? Before I die I'm going to ban bloody muffins from my funeral."

Kev was admitted to Ward 5 North for his second round of chemotherapy. The first one had been successfully administered in the day clinic, but this was apparently another level of difficulty. This complex combination of drugs was aimed at prevention, we were told, rather than cure.

"We're targeting the brain this time," the specialist said.

"But I don't have cancer in my brain," Kev said, running through his mental checklist. Stomach. Back. Check. Shadows on the liver, oesophagus, lung. Had we missed something?

"Do I?"

"You don't have cancer in your brain," the specialist echoed. "But we don't want it to go there. Do we?"

A rhetorical question of the highest order. We said nothing.

It seemed to me to defy logic, that you would decimate a whole lot of healthy blood cells to prevent cancer in an area that didn't have cancer. But when the person you love is too fatigued, too ill, too feverish, to even stand up you don't feel inclined to challenge the experts.

When alarm bells ring, you silence them. You just hand over the trust to the people who have framed certificates hanging on the hospital walls.

This round of chemo was administered as he lay in bed, nurses pecking at his arms trying to find veins so riddled with holes they had gone into hiding. Several bags of drugs emptied into his body and it would be a day or two before his metabolism was able to regroup enough for him to leave hospital.

It didn't, it couldn't.

His body couldn't tolerate this chemo cocktail and his liver ALT levels suddenly rocketed off the charts. The priority order rapidly changed. Suddenly it was not about cancer, it was about correcting liver function. Quickly.

"Get the doctor," someone urged. And people scattered.

The liver is the body's second largest organ, behind the skin. It performs a raft of essential functions related to digestion, metabolism, immunity and the storage of nutrients within the body. Without it, the body would quickly die from the lack of energy and nutrients. So when things go wrong, the race is on to fix them.

You can gauge the seriousness of the problem by the numbers of doctors rushing through, the speed of the nurses' reactions, the number of times they return to check on him, flip through his charts, take blood samples.

There's another indicator too: Google. Mainly I had resisted the temptation to check out Kev's status and prognosis online. I knew it would mess with my own mental state. But, this time, Google lured me in and I scrolled some health sites. It was not good. Out of control liver function in a system already compromised by cancer and chemotherapy had been lethal on too many occasions to count.

There was a very real chance he wouldn't be coming home.

Kev lay in his bed, growing paler, weaker. He trekked back and forth to the bathroom all night to either urinate or vomit. On one of those journeys he fell and lay sprawling on the shiny floor until the nurses found him. His only remaining shred of independence was taken from him: he'd been given a bed pan and confined to bed.

ALT levels — the amount of a particular enzyme — are a reliable measure of liver function. In a healthy organ the level is 10-56; Kev's was 170 and rising. Each time I came back into his room he seemed to have aged a few years. His chatter had dried up; he stared blankly at the ceiling.

I needed a distraction tactic.

"What's the deepest bunker you've ever played out of?" I asked, grappling for a hazard analogy he would buy into. Bunkers in golf represented risk, peril, menace.

The answer came quickly. His brain was muddled, but it seemed to clear when talking about golf.

"Hell Bunker in Las Vegas.

"What's it like?"

"The hole's a copy of the 14th hole at St Andrews, par five. It's an ordinary par five, looks like it has lots of options but there's a deadly dangerous horse-shoe bunker in the middle of the fairway."

I could see him thinking. "It's like playing out of a cave. It's 10 feet tall with a big grassy lip on the top of it. It's killed off some of the best players in the game.

Too much information Norks. Poor choice of words, too.

I had wanted to illustrate that just as there was always a shot you could play to get out of a hazard, there was always something you could do in the face of illness. But this bunker sounded impossible. I could feel my strategy failing.

"So what'd you do?"

"Played smart. Played the odds," he said simply.

"It would have beaten me if I'd taken it on. The only way out was to go backwards.

"Did it work?"

He shrugged.

"Depends on your definition of success," he said. "I went backwards but I finished the round."

Kev's roommate was an elderly woman who had streams of visitors, speaking in hushed voices. A daughter bearing flowers. A hospice worker arranging transfer out of hospital. A lawyer bringing will documents. A minister bringing peace of mind. In the middle of the night she called her son who was living out of town.

"Anthony. Anthony. Where are my scissors?"

Two hours later.

"Anthony. Anthony. I can't find my glasses."

Long nights in hospital. Longer days. Little sleep. "I can't make a complaint about her," Kev said. "She's dying."

The two days we had set aside for this chemo round morphed into four. Then five and six. His liver scores were still off the charts, no longer rising — but not dropping either.

We kept our routines. I arrived every morning at eight to help him shower, shave and dress. We did it to anchor the day, give it a starting point. He would be sitting up in bed, waiting. On the sixth morning he was lying down, pretending to be asleep. He'd been taken off his anti-nausea drugs — another attempt to get the liver function under control — and been up all night vomiting.

I shook him gently, joking about being lazy.

He opened one eye. "I'm not doing it."

I waited. He'd been optimistic since his diagnosis. But the acute illness, the exhaustion, the failure of his body to pick up from this round of chemo, and get back in the game, was beating him down.

"I'm not having a shower."

"Come on," I coaxed. "It's a good start to the day."

"NO. I DON'T WANT TO."

"You have to. We agreed. Each day's a new day. We have to put a stamp on it."

"I'M NOT HAVING A FUCKING SHOWER." He drew the blanket higher and turned over, his back to me.

Anger. I was ready for it. He'd been passive till now, the good boy, doing what he was told. Some defiance was probably a good thing. But I needed to counter it. Anger and passivity were a dangerous combination in a place where dying was the norm.

"Listen Norks," I raised my voice. It seemed to echo off the white walls.

"I'm going to leave you alone for a while, go down the hall and make myself a coffee. And while I'm gone I want you to think about something. This ward is full of people who are dying, they're not coming home. They can stay in bed all day long because it's not going to make any bloody difference. You — as far as I can tell — are still alive. So you decide. Which side of the line do you want to be on?"

I turned and left the ward, my heart hammering inside my ribs.

When I came back 20 minutes later he was sitting on the edge of the bed, his spindly legs dangling over the side. His hair had begun to fall out and greying clumps dotted the shoulders of his black sports shirt. His shower bag and a fresh shirt sat on his knee.

He grinned at me, deathly pale. "Let's do it," he said.

"I don't wanna act like a dead person."

"She is His Only Need"

(Excerpt from Song Performed by Wynonna Judd)

…And my, how the time did fly
The babies grew up and moved away
Left 'em sitting on the front porch rocking
And Billy watching Bonnie's hair turn gray

And ev'ry once in a while you could see him get up
And he'd head downtown
'Cause he heard about something she wanted
And it just had to be found
Didn't matter how simple or how much
It was love
And, boy, ain't that love just something
When it's strong enough to keep a man goin'

Over the line
Working overtime
To give her things just to hear her say she don't
deserve them
But he loves her and he just kept going overboard
Over the limit to afford to give her things he knew
she wanted
'Cause without her where would he be?

See, it's not for him
She is his only need.

Chapter 15

THE VOW

"I'm sorry," Kev said one morning. "This is not what you signed on for."

He was just out of hospital after his brush with death via liver dysfunction. His planned two-day stayover had turned into 12. His liver was operating normally again but the experience had slayed him, physically and mentally, and his third round of chemo had had to be put on hold.

He sat most of the day in his armchair, dozing or staring out the window, watching a flock of tui chortling in the cabbage trees.

"I've really messed up your life."

I was standing at the kitchen bench, counting out his

morning intake of pills and medicine. I looked over at him, hunched in his chair, grey-faced, a box of tissues and a blood thinning injection syringe on the table beside him. He had a red blanket draped across his knees. His nose streamed constantly because all his nose hair had fallen out.

The words "in sickness and in health" played over in my mind.

For better and for worse.

For richer, for poorer.

In sickness and in health.

Wedding vows. When you take those vows, they're just words. How would they be anything else? You're at the start line, on the cusp of a new life, filled with excitement and hope. But marriage is an utter leap of faith because you don't know what's coming. You don't know what time and life will throw at your partner. You don't know what it will throw at you.

If you did, you might choose another path.

My mind skated back to the first steps on the path we had chosen.

A few months into our engagement Kev and I had broken up. I can't recall exactly why, possibly just that we'd gotten together so quickly: weeks after getting engaged we had moved to a new city, were living together and had started new jobs.

It all felt too much. In those days I found it difficult to hold down a job for more than a few months, let alone a relationship. Marriage seemed to me like something I wouldn't be capable of doing for long, let alone well.

Back then, my only communication strategy when things got tough was to run. A necessary ending. Freedom over commitment, every time.

So we ended it.

But — weirdly for me — I really missed him. His steadiness, his dumb puns, the laughs, the pure ease of spending time together.

So, three weeks into our break up, I agreed to meet up. A catch-up that was probably a date. Kev was wearing a blue and white checked flannel shirt, freshly washed but not ironed; his hair was damp from the shower. He had a razor cut on his chin. He always shaved in the mornings, even on weekends.

"I don't feel clean if I don't," he always said. It might have also been to do with the prospect of having a beard by nightfall.

We had free tickets to be in the live audience of a new television dating show. It was terrible and we laughed harder at our lame choice of outing than we did at the show. But — hey — it was free.

Later in Kev's car, a leaky mustard Honda that smelled of mould, we chatted and listened to his well-worn music cassettes, music we had thrashed during several long car rides. A country song came on that we knew by heart.

Kev turned it up. The song, called *She is His Only Need*, was a syrupy tune about this couple called Billy and Bonnie. Kev, ever the romantic, thought it was a tale of great devotion; I thought Billy and Bonnie both needed to get lives.

Anyway Billy was this hard-working loner who couldn't get a girl. He meets Bonnie, they go to a few movies, marry, have two babies. They remain devoted and happy despite what seemed to me the crippling boredom of their lives. Their kids grow up, move away and there they are: "sitting on the front porch…rocking. Billy watching Bonnie's hair turn grey."

"That's us," Kev said as Wynonna Judd's voice filled the car.

"You'll look really cute with white hair. You'll be nodding away on the deck with a blanket and I'll be running back and forth to the kitchen bringing you all your pills."

I laughed, secretly admiring his vision. For a man who hated goal setting, he had a clear mental picture of how the future would be.

"We're not even back together yet," I said. "And you've got the rocking chairs out."

His turn to chuckle. "I can see the future and you're rocking that chair."

"In your dreams buddy."

"Wait and see," he said.

Really? I wondered now, trying to decipher my way through the bottles of medication lining the bench. Is this what it has come to? Is this how it's going to be?

Nursing was not one of my strengths, nor, if I'm honest, was sympathy for physical ills. Luckily I'd married a man of robust good health, to whom sick days were something to be avoided, were really just there for the weak and infirm.

Over the years I'd been fine with his rare spells in bed for stomach bugs or flu. I'd been dutiful and caring, the kindly purveyor of chicken soup, even if it was poured from a can and heated at pace. I was even composed when he collapsed one night in searing pain and was rushed to hospital where doctors hovered until they diagnosed the mystery illness.

Ping. A kidney stone.

"The doctors say the pain is the male equivalent of having a baby," Kev told me later, proudly, holding up the offending stone — a spit of gravel in a small plastic jar. I doubted this, by the way, but let him have his moment.

The truth was that I was not really up for having a husband so disabled by cancer that he couldn't walk. I didn't want to have my living room looking like a bad hybrid of a retirement home and a hospital. I did not want to lie awake all night in terror of a fall as he trailed back and forth to the bathroom on his walker. I did not want to be a fulltime caregiver or a maid. Most of all, I did not want to have my once independent, capable, high energy husband so utterly reliant on me. For everything.

But what do you do?

I kept counting out the pills. It was an arduous job; the drugs all had complicated names and I'd had to get the cancer nurse to colour code them for me. Apricot for constipation, yellow for nausea, white for stomach bacteria, pink fluid for digestion, hiccups, stomach bacteria. A daily injection to thin his blood. A kiwifruit flush to follow so that his bowel function wouldn't gum up.

"I know this is crap for you," Kev said.

"Hey, it's just part of the deal," I said with fake goodwill. "You'd do it for me."

"Of course I would. But I think it's better this way round. I'd be a blubbering mess. I wouldn't be able to bear seeing you sick."

We were both silent for a moment. It was actually true, but I didn't want to say so. I was more pragmatic, more emotionally contained, better able to cope with the pain and fear of seeing him so sick, or facing the likelihood he would die well before the expiry date we had in mind.

Or maybe I just bottled it better?

And Kev made a braver and more cheerful patient than I would have been with my health and looks and dignity stripped away. At least that's what we thought. You don't know really until you're there.

"I'm lucky you're tough," Kev said.

I tipped the tablets and capsules into the pill box so they were sorted into morning, afternoon and evening. Yellow. Orange. Apricot. White.

Tough, I thought to myself. Yeah I'm tough. So tough that I cried all through my run that morning. And every run at the moment because it's the one place I could afford to let go, didn't have to keep the mask on, nodding and smiling and pretending I thought everything was going to be ok.

"I don't think you're lucky I'm tough. I think you're lucky I like you."

"Well, I wouldn't blame you if you didn't right now."

"You're even more lucky I liked you before you got sick. If I didn't I don't know how careful I'd be measuring out these pills."

He laughed but it was a little edgy.

I thought, not for the first time, of all those people who were struggling in their relationships when cancer or ill-fortune struck, people who were considering leaving when the cage dropped and trapped them.

Cancer doesn't wipe out all the niggles in relationships; it exaggerates them. It certainly doesn't make relationships easier. It makes them way, way harder.

In the beginning everyone is aiming at survival, at "beating this thing". But that's only part of it: there are other fears too — work, money, kids — and what it all means for the future.

Not only what if Kev dies.

But what if he lives? What if he's different? Looks different? What if I don't — can't — look at him in the same way. What if he's a different man and WHAT IF I don't like that man? What if I want to run but I'm trapped. I mean, what kind of bitch leaves the Cancer Guy?

Runaway thoughts.

A young woman whose partner was ravaged with cancer once told me that his body was so wrecked and poisoned by the disease that she was frightened of it. He still wanted sex, she could barely bring herself to touch him. How could she deny him, a dying man? Her guilt consumed her.

What if that happened to me?

These are not questions you can take out into the world. You have to lock them down. You have to appear loving, not scared. There is no gain in hurling a psychological hand grenade into the mix.

But I knew what was going on here. Mental illness had showed me, taught me well. Anxiety. Trauma. Alcoholism. Drugs. Depression. Suicide. I knew it didn't just affect the person at the centre of it. I knew it spread, snaked, through families, testing partners, kids, wider families, aunties and uncles, brothers and sisters, parents. It was like a tsunami. The illness was the wave, that's the dramatic bit, that's often when people step up. You often see the best of people because they have something to do. But the thing that really tests people isn't the wave, it's what's left on the beach afterwards. The debris. The emotional chaos. The struggle to put their lives back together when the foundation of them has been wiped out.

My mind drifted to one of my first clients when I started in private practice. He was a man in his early 40s with chronic depression. He was a talented artist and once he got a brush back in his hand he literally painted his way out of his gloom. But, as he rose to the surface, his strong, capable partner went down. Years of worry and fear, of picking up the load, of tiptoeing around his illness, and training their three children to do the same so they wouldn't push him over the edge, took a toll and she found herself in the grips of a depressive episode, panic attacks disabling her function and her confidence.

Suddenly the "rock" was incapacitated and the family she had held together for so long fell apart. Her husband, my client, did not have the emotional skills to take her place. Their elder son leaned on his cannabis habit, their daughter developed an eating disorder, the youngest son was out of control at school. The woman's distressed parents struggled to cope. It showed me up close how far mental illness can reach, what it does to families and, ever since, I have tried to think beyond the person in my care, to their partners and parents and children.

The person who gets ill is the victim and, potentially, the hero. But there is nothing heroic about being the partner of a sick person. There is not much fun in it, either. Sometimes I have wondered why the partners of unwell people stay with them because it's such an exhausting job, mentally and physically.

It's a job for a saint. Or a martyr. And, scarily, I was neither of those.

That's what I thought now, as I screwed the lids back on the bottles and snapped the pill boxes closed, as I wandered across the room to deliver Kev's morning selection of pills and potions.

Could I do this? Could I keep doing this?

I picked up the syringe and he rolled up his shirt so I could inject his bruised stomach. "Just do what you have to do," I told myself, ripping the hygiene tab off the needle.

But my mind wouldn't stay in the moment. It was off its leash and running.

What lies ahead? It shrieked inside my head.

Where the hell is this going to land?

Article published in the Dominion Post, December 2012

THE SUMMER THAT CHANGED MY LIFE

By Kevin Norquay

After five years cloistered in a boarding school imagining the joys of life on the outside, December 1973 opened the door to freedom. I had big plans, only to painfully learn how swiftly all could go astray.

As I lay in the 20-bed dormitory I had called home for so long, I plotted. I would play my records as loud as I pleased; short back and sides haircuts would be replaced — I would adorn my face with sideburns, a moustache, with a shaggy rock star "do" providing the icing.

While roaming the roads and beaches, I would try to meet mysterious creatures known as girls, so far seen only from a distance as they walked past to the Marist College, or briefly and awkwardly encountered at dancing classes and one-off balls.

I would travel north to Dargaville, join a hay gang, make stacks of money while the sun shone, and enter university rich, muscular and tanned.

There would be no more getting up about 7am daily to a clanging bell and exercises, no more mass-produced meals, no more getting out for only a few hours each Sunday, no more compulsory church.

I'd miss the friendships, but not the regimentation.

I would not face this heroic quest alone. Co-inmates Vern Woods and Ian Purdie had a shared vision, as well as a passion for loud blues and rock music.

We were all part of fledgling band Molehill, named in deference to American power quartet Mountain, who in Leslie West had a vocalist whose strangled and tuneless vocals I could emulate.

The final, most vital, piece of the dream was a 1963 Austin Mini, a sparkling deep blue with a black vinyl roof that set it apart from the more common versions. It was my first car, and I loved it.

Six days after my father shelled out $695 for it, I wrote it off. Not in spectacular rock star fashion; the Mini had a top speed of only 100kmh. I was doing half that when I made the mistake of glancing at the gear lever while changing down, veering on to the gravel verge then over-correcting.

My prized-possession rolled four-and-a-half times, its driver emerging uninjured but for a piece of windscreen glass stuck deep in the back of the right hand. About an hour into my trip to Dargaville, my summer dream died in a screech of metal and a shattering of glass on the Bombay Hills.

While unhurt, I was a mental mess. I was traumatised. I still have a gravel-phobia. I tense up in cars that are making a down hill approach to a sharp left intersection, as I was on December 2, 1973.

When the Mini was put the right way up, it sat all four wheels askew, its vinyl roof in shreds. It looked as if it had been on an all night bender at a series of bars. Shocked, I climbed into the driver's seat and made to drive off.

Motorists who had stopped to help had to convince me I was going nowhere.

For weeks after I wept when my mind revisited the crash, or when I was criticised for attempting such a long journey — Hamilton to Dargaville — with such little driving experience (my critics were right, I can see now).

On top of my mental scars, I was skint and had no transport. Plans had to be remade. Vern and I wound up painting my grandparents' house in sleepy Pukekohe.

They were kindly, thoughtful and non-judgmental, and that helped put my mental pieces back in place. For all that, spending the evening watching the wedding of Princess Anne and Mark Phillips on their television was far from what we had in mind as high-life entertainment when we quit boarding school.

Of the initial blueprint for the summer, it seemed only growing facial hair remained a possibility. I set about that task with a bristling energy.

In lieu of a car or money, we discovered hitch-hiking. Safety considerations were never raised; it was two years before Mona Blades went missing while hitching near Taupo, and we thought ourselves bullet-proof — it was probably safer than my driving, in any event.

So we hitched and we hiked, with varying degrees of success. As a trio, our rides were limited to short hops. A pair did better, while going solo was better still if you needed to cover long distances.

Back together, we formed ourselves into a weedy

shambolic urbanite hay gang, working for a contractor in the Waihue Valley north of Dargaville.

In those days, hay bales weighing about 40kg bound together by two strips of twine or wire, were loaded on to a truck using an escalator-like device that picked them off the ground and moved them to above truck deck level.

Once it had a full load, the truck would take the bales to a hayshed, where they would be unloaded to be stored as winter feed.

It was back-breaking hard work outside in the blazing sun, or head-bashing hard work inside, where rafters seemed to take every opportunity to give your head a crisp clunking, particularly late at night when you were exhausted and couldn't see a damned thing.

As the tallest, Vern was distributor at the top of the elevator, flicking the bales this way and that to Ian and myself to slam into place, an interlocking jigsaw puzzle of fragrant fodder.

Poorly stacked bales had a nasty habit of falling off the truck, and if that happened you'd have to reload them all by hand. When the truck was moving across the side of a hill, you'd hold your breath as cracks in the load appeared.

In such cases Ian was peril personified — his mad and clumsy scrambling for safety at times causing him to shunt off half the stack with his feet, to a chorus of groans and his own protestations of complete innocence.

Corrugated iron haysheds were stinking hot, bailing twine ripped the skin from your hands, and prickly thistles abounded in some crops.

But it was fun — we got muscles, we got tans and we made a slick team we are still proud of and think of often, nearly 40 years on. Our band penned the still unheralded masterpiece Goat Parts, and listened rapt to Jimi Hendrix, Cream, an array of blues bands, and Mountain.

"Goat parts, all over the road, that goat we hit sure did explode," I sung, as the radio airwaves tended toward Time in a Bottle by Jim Croce, the 1974 Commonweath Games theme song Join Together and Big Norm, a quirky tribute to Prime Minister Norman Kirk.

We were able to repeat our magical hay-music-sunshine formula for the next two summers, until inevitably we went our separate ways, to Otago, Massey and Waikato Universities and from there around the world.

Now, Vernon is back in Dargaville, Ian is in Sydney. Both still play in bands, none of us hitch-hike, two of us are bald.

My baldness is chemically induced, after being told in July I had acquired a malignant tumour of the spine, and a more placid one in the stomach.

There were tears, as there had been in the wake of the car wreck disaster of 1973. And there was hope and optimism.

If I learned anything from that summer, it was that one disaster need not crush your dreams, that anything is possible once you climb from the wreckage, especially if you have great friends and a loving family.

As I do, yet again.

Chapter 16

OUT OF THE ROUGH

I got up early one morning and went in search of my brown leather satchel, which was still lying in the spare room where I'd abandoned it a couple of months earlier. It contained my diary, pens, tissues: tools of my trade.

"I'm going to work," I said to Kev, carrying the satchel back into the bedroom. "You'll be ok here for a few hours won't you?"

"But you don't have an office."

It was true. I'd given up my room in the city so I didn't have to pay rent while he was sick. But I figured I could practice without a room of my own, at least for a little while. One of my clients had suggested we meet for a walk on the waterfront. Another wanted to meet in a café, a third in a hotel lobby.

"Who needs an office?" I said brightly, trying not to worry about the lack of confidentiality in cafes and hotels. "This is psych-to-go."

He smiled. "OK psycho-to-go. I'll make you some breakfast." He eased his heavy legs out of bed.

I needed to go back to work: I had a practice to run. It's not the sort of job where you can just close up shop. People have trusted you with their secrets and fears, they are relying on you to hold those things safe. You need a very good reason for cutting them loose before they are ready.

Cancer had given me that good reason. But — still — I worried about them. And, truthfully, I worried about myself.

Part of me was terrified of going back in the therapy room for fear that I wouldn't be able to give my clients what they needed. Would I be able to concentrate for a full hour without being distracted by my own problems? Would I be more easily upset at the sadness, and sometimes horror, of people's lives? Would I be dismissive — or even scornful — of a woman wanting to cut down on her daily chocolate intake when I was navigating life and death at home?

But certainly I wasn't the only mental health worker to ply their trade with their personal life fractured.

I had to go back. My clients needed me — even my procrastinator was asking for an appointment — and in a strange way I needed them. Work was my normality.

I couldn't keep standing at the bus stop. I had to get on board.

There was something else, too. Money.

Kev's employer, Fairfax NZ, had been very supportive of his illness and after a couple of months off work he was still on full pay. As I was self employed and had stopped working to look after him I had no income. We had savings, but we also had a mortgage, bills, kids to support. We had a future to think about too, although the length of that was up for debate. Naturally we were concerned about money, worried that if Kev didn't get back to work we'd be strapped for cash, our options limited. Especially if I had to stay home to look after him.

A few days earlier our insurance broker had come to our house. Kev, fresh out of hospital and having his mortality slapped in his face, had invited him over to talk through *Our Options*. He had also booked an appointment at the Public Trust office to get our wills updated. He didn't spell it out but I understood the subtext: if I'm going to die, I want my family to be in good shape financially. It was more commonly known as getting your affairs in order.

Malcolm Montgomery, our broker, was a short, broad man in an impeccably fitted dark suit, a blue shirt and a mauve and white striped tie. His left hand was adorned with two heavy gold signet rings. His shirt cuffs were pinned with chunky gold cufflinks.

He sat carefully on our worn and faded sofa, laid a folder on the coffee table, and talked through our policies. Our dog Tommy sniffed at his polished shoes.

He had a radio voice, low and melodic. Just right for talking about money and death, arguably the two emotional topics on the planet. Along with sex, of course.

We listened. We listened some more. Then we asked about entitlements.

There were none. Well, there were plenty — if Kev died.

"Is it a terminal illness?" Malcolm asked, looking down at the folder. Because if you can get a letter from your surgeon along those lines then things look quite different. You could get an immediate $50,000 payout. That would ease things."

Along those lines?

"You mean if I'm definitely going to die?" Kev said.

Malcolm nodded.

Kev and I looked at each other.

It was one thing to be gravely ill and staring down the barrel of death, it was another to have a written proof that you were not going to recover.

We probably could get such a letter from the oncologists, they hadn't masked the seriousness of the situation from us. But we both knew that psychologically it would throw us into a space that would not be helpful, one we were not ready for.

Eradicating hope was a foolish game to play.

"No," we said almost in unison. "We're not there yet."

"I understand," said Malcolm Montgomery, smoothly brokering the gap back from the precipice of death into the land of the living. He looked at us with sincerity. The best salesmen are well versed in human reaction, they know how to tap the right emotion at the right time. He would know uncertainty drives up angst, and that's what propels people to sign up for insurance.

So then he hit on me. Appropriately.

"Karen do you have income protection insurance?"

"Not currently." True answer: never. I should — BUT. It was expensive. The dance of the self-employed.

"What if you were to get sick? Now. With Kevin unable to work as well."

He let the words hang, the pictures form. Two sick people. Loss of two incomes. High degree of fear.

"What would it cost?" I asked, suddenly vulnerable. "Ballpark amount?"

He tapped at the screen of his cellphone, running some numbers and floated a few figures. The weekly premiums sounded like extortion when my current income was nil.

"We'll get back to you," I said, getting to my feet and waiting for Malcolm to do the same.

"At the moment we need our money for food."

Less than a week later I was dressed for work, fortified for battle with the two eggs Kev had poached for me while leaning unsteadily on the kitchen bench.

"Are you sure you'll be ok? I'm only seeing two clients. I'll be back at lunchtime."

"I'll be great," he said, almost too quickly, tapping at his phone at the same time. As I turned to head out the door I noticed he was putting his shoes on. Weird. It was not like he could go for a walk. He had no balance and his feet hit the ground like slabs of concrete. He couldn't even get down the front steps by himself.

"Going somewhere?" I said, watching as he grappled with his shoe. I didn't really mean it though: just a throw away line.

"Well," he mumbled, averting his eyes from me, looking guilty. A man who could never keep a secret.

"The boys are picking me up. We thought we might go to the driving range."

So we began to make our way back. Out of the rough, onto the fairway.

Kev's chemotherapy had settled into a three-week cycle, provided his temperature stayed down and his blood cells recovered sufficiently in three weeks to take another hammering. The regularity of the cycle gave us a framework to hang his recovery on. We were Friday people; that meant we had the Friday chemo nurses — Kirsty and Amy — and we looked forward to catching up with them and all the other Friday people, hooked up to their drips, some bright and chirpy, others desperately ill and devoid of hope.

We tried to make these Fridays fun. We'd bring coffee, a pile of magazines or a book and banter with the nurses, the patients who were up for it and their supporters. We always had a plan to do something straight after each six-hour treatment, no matter how exhausted Kev felt, just to keep everything feeling balanced and normal. On a good day we'd hit the golf driving range or go to a movie. When nausea or fatigue took hold, the back-up plan was a spin around an appliance or hardware mega store in the wheelchair or spend half an hour on a park bench by the sea.

Lunch — or any form of non-bland eating — was clearly not an option.

We'd arrive at the day clinic intent on seeking out prime position, the armchairs next to the windows.

"Race you to the window seats," we'd say to the woman with breast cancer who couldn't run because her legs were swollen with lymphedema — the fallout of a double mastectomy that had wrecked her lymphatic system. She and her friend would laugh at Kev's lame attempt to sprint with his concrete-loaded legs.

We were there, in the chemo clinic, the year Lance Armstrong, seven times tour de France cycling champion and cancer hero was exposed as a drug cheat. It had led during one chemo session to a lively debate.

When Kev was first diagnosed, Tess, reaching for a way forward, had said "you're going to be just like Lance Armstrong dad — only not a wanker."

We had all chuckled.

Now, as the toxic chemicals flowed, it was harder to judge. Armstrong was also just a man who had been where we were now. With his worldwide *Live Strong* trust and campaign he had done an awful lot of good for a lot of people.

"Bad for cycling, good for cancer," the breast cancer woman said, neatly packaging his choices and her views, and we all nodded. Empathy comes easier to the vulnerable.

I'd been given four yellow *Live Strong* wristbands, which Kev and me, and the girls, had committed to wearing: a show of solidarity.

"Should we ditch the wristbands?" Kev asked when Armstrong's cheating was confirmed.

A short debate. We needed all the help on offer. *Live Strong* was a good mantra. We kept them on.

Between rounds of chemo, Kev went back to work. At first for a few hours a day, popping into the office where everyone told him how wonderful he looked. He did not look good. What they meant was he looked better than they expected. That was, I reasoned, because they expected him to be dead. He did look better than a dead person but, to be honest, I didn't think the gap between the two was huge.

Work was therapy for him; as a news editor he loved the action, the ebb and flow of the news. He loved the people too, the banter, the cynicism. There, he had his place, he felt valued. But there's nothing like a newsroom for making you feel the utter impermanence of your life. Journalists can be cocky but they know they're not indispensable. It doesn't matter who you are when you die, the news keeps breaking, the presses keep rolling all through the night.

"If I died the newspaper would still come out," Kev said.

I nodded. "The very next day. And the day after that."

"You work hard and you think you're a big deal — but you're not," he said, acknowledging that everything in the newsroom had kept ticking over in his absence. "In the end, I'm totally unnecessary."

"A message to us all," I said, meaning it.

I gave up on psych-to go after a couple of months and moved back into a room, hiring it from a colleague for a few hours a week. She offered me a permanent lease but I was too frightened to commit. What if something went wrong with the treatment again? What if the cancer spread? What if?

But at least I was back in business.

After my initial fears, I found seeing clients was helpful for my own mental state. It allowed me — for one hour at a time — to climb out of my hole and to listen to someone else's story, to enter their world, to focus on their problems. It reminded me that the universe did not revolve around me. That cancer wasn't all that was going on in the world. That no matter what was happening for us, people still had their own difficulties to deal with and by seeing clients I could keep some perspective. As well as giving me something to do professionally — and an income — it was almost therapeutic in that it forced me outside of the bubble that cancer had blown around us.

Ironically, or perhaps because I had to take a conscious step away from myself, I found myself doing some really good work, my thoughts were crisp and I brought greater understanding into therapy.

My sense of humour, which had taken a pummelling in real life, was intact with my clients — and I was grateful for that. Therapy felt almost like fun, the way it had when I had first started in practice. Although it may have been simply that I had stepped off the treadmill for a while; now I had only a handful of clients so I could take my time and savour each hour.

A few clients asked where I'd been. I told them, releasing only as much detail as they asked for, as I could handle.

One young woman, who was struggling with health anxiety, wasn't satisfied with the scant details I gave in reply to her questions. Any niggles and pains in her own body caused her to catastrophise, to imagine the worst possible outcome, which usually involved tumours and led to her dying by ravaging cancer and/or horrific pain.

So hearing of Kev's cancer fanned her anxiety. She needed to know more. What kind of cancer was it? What were the warning signs? What had the doctors missed? What had WE failed to pick up on?

I told her. She looked stricken.

What's wrong?" I said.

She laughed nervously. "You're not going to believe this. I've had a sore back lately."

Chapter 17

THE MENTAL GAME

"How are the stress levels?" I asked one morning, as we were getting ready for work.

Kev didn't reply, he was too busy digging in a drawer for two socks that matched, his mind already skittering around the newsroom. He was back working full time and he'd just had his first dream about work in months.

Outwardly Kev had the kiwi bloke "just deal with it" persona; he was calm under pressure, a multi-tasker in the newsroom, able to fire-spot disaster even with his back to it.

Inwardly, though, he could get wound tight as a top: be sensitive to criticism and defensive under attack. I could always tell when he was stressed because he'd walk faster, ums and ahs would begin to pepper his speech and his shoulder muscles would tense and rise, making him look hunched and short in the neck.

"Relax," I'd say, tapping his shoulders and he'd grin guiltily and consciously drop them down.

We'd talked a little bit about the role stress might have played in his cancer. He'd been under a lot of pressure in the months before he was diagnosed; the New Zealand Press Association was going through a protracted closing and, as the editor, he was being squeezed from both sides: the Board above him, and the staff below. He had a lot of unhappy and worried people beating on his door. He'd come home at night full of the drama of other people's lives: their jobs, their finances, their relationships, their futures. It was something I was used to leaving in my room when I shut my office door, but Kev kept caring after hours — he carried a heavy load.

I believed that stressful period had triggered the cancer in his already vulnerable body — but the research didn't support that view.

Science had recognized that stressful events altered hormone and cortisol levels, so affecting the immune system. But, despite the many studies, there was no conclusive evidence that these changes could lead to cancer.

Believe what you will. When you work in mental health you know what emotional distress can do to a person's physical health. You know the damage it can cause.

I'd seen it over and over again. Cancers. Chronic Fatigue. M.E. Eating Disorders. Obesity. Muscular Diseases.

Irritable Bowel Syndrome. Heart attacks. Migraines. A myriad of unexplained aches and pains.

I knew. I also knew my husband better than any researcher ever would.

I understood that being armed to deal with stress, with being able to turn down the internal noise, was essential to his full recovery.

But he'd scorned my hints about learning to meditate, even when I disguised it as "deep relaxation" and talked it up as a proven means of lowering stress levels and relieving pain.

"Meditation would also help your immunity and hormone levels. And it's good for blood pressure and circulation" I said, knowing I was talking more to myself.

He sat across from me now, on the edge of the bed, struggling to reach his foot to put his socks on. I'd stopped helping a while ago, knowing he wanted to be independent.

"I'm not bloody meditating," he said. "I'm not getting up at 5am to sit in a corner chanting and humming. It's a waste of time when I could be putting."

"OK smart arse — but you need a way of unwinding — emotionally. You need a way of forgetting about work, about everything, and — just — breathing."

He looked up, gleeful, the battle with the sock forgotten.

"Golf is my meditation. Hum. Hummmmmmm."

I didn't like to point out that golf hadn't stopped the cancer invasion first time round. Still, on another level it was true. There was something almost hypnotic about the effect the little ball had on him. With his focus on each shot, it was difficult for him to think about anything else. I'd seen him begin a round tense and wired, and end it loose and relaxed. Golf would work if we packaged it for mental — as well as physical — gain.

There was a problem, though.

"Aren't you forgetting a rather large barrier to this plan? You can't walk."

"Yes. Well." He picked up his sock again. "There's something I've been meaning to talk to you about. ..."

He and his mate Tim bought an electric cart they stored in a shed at their beloved Karori Golf Club. Kev was touched when Tim's father-in-law Garry Evans gave them $1000 towards it — $500 each. Dubbed the "Timonator" (a hybrid of their golf nicknames Timbo and Norkinator), it was pimped up: fluffy pom poms swung in the cabin, a custom made number plate, stick-men figures stuck on the windows, Timonator branded pens in the glove box.

Three months after diagnosis he was back on the first tee. Bald, wobbly and needing help to get up to some of the tee boxes, his first drive went 100 metres shorter than usual. His second, he missed the ball. He shot 112. His best was 78. No matter, his spirits rose.

As his health improved and he could drive the car again, he would head out to the golf course and play a round by himself. One day he was late coming home. Very late. I called his cell phone, worrying. No reply. I called again, my heart starting to race.

Where was he? Had he tripped, collapsed? Who could I get to go find him? I was running through the options when he burst through the door, limping even more than usual, the knee torn out of his golf pants, dirt sticking to the side of his face.

"What happened?" I asked.

"86, best score of the summer," he beamed.

I frowned.

"OK I crashed," he said. "Got thrown out of the cart."

"What?"

"The cart slid down the hill in the dew and I got tossed. It ran over my foot."

"Great headline," I said, shaking my head. "Man survives cancer then is killed by his own golf cart."

He laughed. "I need to be more careful."

Was it therapy, the golf? Yes.

It had all the components: Something to do, something to aim for, fresh air, a way to relax, time with his mates. It was a barometer of recovery.

He set tiny goals, checking each one off, with a flash of triumph. Each outing the ball went a little further, his balance was a little better, on steep slopes a supportive shoulder from a mate was needed less and less.

He switched from a white ball to a Cancer Society yellow, for a visual reminder that just being able to play and be among friends was a blessing, even if his clubs had to double as walking sticks.

Five months after he'd landed in hospital he played on the Boys Golf Weekend (BGW), the tournament he, Tim and Kevvy Kane had created seven years earlier. It was held twice a year in February (The Bomb the Green Invitational) and November (The Lampshade Classic), with craft beer fuelled "committee meetings" held all year round. For the 2012 Lampshade Classic, all 18 of the boys turned up wearing wigs in various styles and colours, a quiet nod to the cancer journey.

Within weeks of chemo ending, he notched best-ever scores on three courses. His handicap was its lowest in five years.

We didn't need to be told he was in remission. We knew.

Kev was discharged by a doctor we had barely seen during his six months of treatment. That didn't matter to me because I'd been largely invisible, and nameless, to the doctors during the months of appointments: "Kevin attended with his wife," written in the medical notes was the only evidence of my constant presence.

But it mattered to Kev. He would have liked to have received his exit papers from one of the doctors he'd gotten to know well and trusted, that he'd had a few laughs with along the way.

This doctor had a cool, brusque manner and limited skills in diplomacy. Those factors were bearable, but the forecast he dispatched was harder to absorb.

"Well that's it," he said, showing us out the door into the wide, busy corridor. "Your odds are about 60:40. Which is good." I wondered why he hadn't said this while we were in the consulting room — with the door shut. Now he was sharing Kev's prognosis with everyone who wandered past.

I watched Kev pause, turn and look at him.

"What does that mean?"

"Slightly better odds of living a while than dying."

"I would've liked the odds of staying alive a little higher than that."

The doctor nodded. "That's fair. So far, so good though. Lymphoma, as we've discussed, doesn't go away. There is no cure. It'll be back. You might get three years. Good luck."

And he turned away.

"Bit of a prick," Kev was white faced as we walked down the corridor. "Those are not very good odds. Three years isn't very long."

It wasn't uplifting news, but nor was it a shock. It wasn't the kindest delivery either but — I got it — cancer doctors are up against the wall. When you finish treatment patients don't say "thanks for curing me."

On a good day, people might say "thanks for your help, for all you've done for me." But they can't say thanks for the cure because no one really knows where their health is going — or if the cancer's coming back. People walk out of the hospital with a terrible fear that the monster they saw off is still hiding under the bed. Waiting for a chance to pounce.

"That's just his opinion Norks, it's not a given." I tried to reason. "He doesn't know you, the kind of man you are. He doesn't know your attitude, your psychology or your support team. He can't know your future. He certainly can't bring the hammer down on your life."

But I could tell he was worried.

We went out for lunch, a beachside café to celebrate. The air felt heavy, gloomier than at almost any time in the previous six months when his body was being bashed about by treatment. My glass of wine remained untouched. Kev picked at his seafood salad.

"I guess I just have to make the most of things."

"No-one knows how long you've got. Could be ages. You could outlive me. Maybe we just need to play life differently. Both of us."

He speared a piece of poached fish with his fork but didn't raise it to his mouth.

"It just means a shift in the way we think. Instead of the long game, we work on our short one. Maybe it was overdue anyway," I said, almost as an afterthought.

Kev stayed silent.

"It's like cricket," I said, getting a bit desperate, trying to snatch a solution out of the air.

"So what if we're not playing test cricket anymore. We can still play Twenty20."

He smiled. "The short version of the life game. So we have more fun in less time?"

I blew out my breath.

"Exactly," I said.

Chapter 18

SHOCK TREATMENT

I pulled up outside the Breast Clinic.

I was due for a mammogram and with life back to semi-normal I had no excuse for postponing it. While Kev was in chemotherapy I'd been accepted onto the national breast screening programme — which simply means free biannual mammograms for all women over 45 years — and I was here for my appointment.

I had no reason to think I had breast cancer or even abnormal breast tissue. But with the remnants of cancer still evident everywhere I looked, I didn't think it would be wise to flip the bird at checking for it.

I don't enjoy mammograms. Is there a woman alive who does?

I stood at reception, filling in forms, fortified with pain medication. When my name was called, I went behind the curtain, stripped down to my jeans and pulled the pale green x-ray robe over my head. Why do they bother with these robes? It was only three paces from the cubicle to the x-ray machine where I had to take it off again.

The radiographer was a pleasant woman in her fifties, a motherly figure who I imagined weighing herself every morning and sighing because her clothes kept getting tighter.

"You've had some breast soreness?" she asked.

"Yes. Just the last week or so."

"Any chance you are pregnant?"

Was she joking? Clearly she had not looked at my date of birth on the admittance form. Fifty would be quite old to be venturing down that pathway, I would have thought but I figured she had to check.

She looked up at me, clocking my wrinkles and then back at the form.

"I'm way too old for that," I said. "Besides, my husband had a vasectomy 15 years ago."

"Ha. That doesn't mean a thing," she said briskly, half smiling at her own wit. She got down to business, hauling my left breast up and onto the glass plate. My body contorted and I half crouched in trying to satisfy her photographic needs.

She lowered the top glass plate towards my flattened organ. I took a breath and held it.

"Breathe normally!" she snapped, pausing the machine to wrench at my shoulders, one back, one forward.

"I'm sure the mammography was invented by a man," I said, making conversation nervously.

"I mean men would never put themselves through this. Smashing their bits flat between a couple of glass plates until they yelped. Who would think that was a good idea?"

She ignored me and stepped back behind her machine, all concentration.

Truly, it had always struck me that mammograms are a barbaric procedure. That pancaking the breast between glass plates would be more likely to trigger cancer than find it. None of the women I'd known to be diagnosed with breast cancer had discovered it via mammogram — it had been through breast lumps, changes or inconsistencies. Surely there was more sophisticated and accurate way to screen for breast cancer?

But this was not the time for these kinds of thoughts or questions.

She brought the top plate down on my breast, squashing it flat. I groaned.

"Tell me when you can't take it any more," she said.

I waited one second. "I can't take it anymore."

She lowered the plate a couple more millimetres anyway. I shut my eyes and tried to use the imagery techniques, the same as those I had insisted Kev use for chemotherapy.

White light. White light flowing to the source. Melting away the pain. Think. Breathe. Use mantra.

It didn't work at all.

She took some pictures and went through the whole procedure again on the other side. She left the room to view the film and came back into the room, frowning.

"We'll have to repeat the left side. The picture's not clear. The angle was wrong."

Subtext: You moved, you naughty girl.

I sighed. I didn't think it was me who had screwed up the angle.

This mammogram was more painful than I remembered. We finished and she smiled at me. "You can relax. We're done."

Then I thought of something I probably should have mentioned half an hour earlier.

"My husband got sick with cancer six months ago. I stopped getting my period then — and I haven't had one since."

She looked at me, her head to one side. "Was it sudden? His cancer."

"Very," I said. "The ultimate curveball."

"Shock," she said, thinking.

"Are you having night sweats?" she asked.

I shrugged. Yes — but Kev's were worse.

"Mood swings?"

Weird question to put to a cancer caregiver. A bit like asking a new mother if she's tired.

"I guess with the cancer….I've been a bit up and down."

"Sudden onset menopause," she said. "I've seen it many times before. The shock of his illness would have thrown you straight into menopause. It's all the proof I need to know the mind and body are connected."

For a minute I thought she was going to hug me, which

I was not sure I was up for from a woman who'd inflicted such savage pain. Then she tucked the x-ray plate under her arm and turned away. The wait room was full.

I left the clinic in search of more painkillers and a double shot coffee. Both breasts throbbed.

My mammogram was clear.

Three days later I got my period.

Chapter 19

THE VOID

"**I** need to thank people," Kev said.

It was a few days after his discharge from hospital and he was feeling a little lost. Suddenly the framework for cancer — the chemo sessions and the doctors' appointments — had been taken away. The void of discharge gaped in front of us. He missed the hospital, not the place so much as the safety, the certainty of what it offered. We both did, it had given us something solid to hang on to.

Getting into remission was supposed to be a triumph. We knew that; we'd heard the stories about the people who had targeted remission as their goal — and never made it.

But remission held no certainty.

Kev wrote a story for the Dominion Weekend magazine, which likened remission to intermission at the movies: that perhaps he was in the foyer getting ice-cream and lollies before going back into the darkness. There was an unease that cancer could swallow us up again.

"I need to take them some presents just to show my appreciation."

"Good idea," I said. And it was. Happiness gurus the world over advocated showing formal appreciation through journals, daily lists and the like.

But I knew the gift of a pretty journal to record his thanks would be wasted on him. He would rather shell out for some gifts.

"Who are you thinking about?"

He checked them off on his fingers. "Radiologists, hospital staff, chemo nurses, everyone who looked after me."

"That's a lot of presents," said the person who'd be going out to buy them.

"They gave me a lot of help."

Kev was probably the most generous person I'd ever met. A few weeks before his legs gave out I found him in our bedroom rolling up one of his suits and sliding it into a supermarket bag. He then went over to his wardrobe and selected a tie, blue striped, one he sometimes wore.

"I'm giving this to Te Awa," he said.

"Who's Te Awa?" I asked. "And why does he need to have your clothes?"

"He has to go to a wedding this weekend," he said, distracted, shoving the tie into the bag.

"And he doesn't have a thing to wear?"

Te Awa turned out to be the super-charged cheerful young guy who served him coffee every morning in the work cafe. Kev had known him for a couple of weeks.

"Loan or gift?" I asked, knowing the answer.

Kev shrugged. "How many suits can you wear?"

I shook my head. He was the guy who would give you the shirt off his back, literally. Over the years I'd had to stop him giving me things, buying me presents all the time even though I loved it. Every woman likes flowers, but not if it means you can't meet your mortgage payments. I held back many times on mentioning things I wanted because he'd come home with it — or a brochure for it — in his briefcase that night, the beam bright across his face. He liked giving; perhaps even more he liked pleasing people.

Cancer seemed to send him into an orbit of gratitude: for his family, his mates, his life and all that he'd been fortunate to have and do in his 55 years.

The care, the view out the window, even the hospital food came in for rave reviews.

"Are you kidding me?" I said to this latest outburst. I'd tasted the hospital steak and kidney pie, an experience I thought a person only needed once.

"It was delicious," he said, smacking his lips.

As he began to recover his fragile health, the people in his cancer world became the target: the doctors, the chemo nurses, the radiographers, the nurses in the orthopaedic and cancer wards. I encouraged it: feeling and expressing gratitude was proven means of enhancing psychological wellbeing.

So we filled big glass jars with brightly coloured sweets and treats, drove to the hospital, and set off on a Santa Claus-type tour of all the wards.

"What do you reckon they'll say when they see I'm still alive," Kev said, limping unsteadily down the polished corridors. Beside him, I lugged sports bags full of cards and gifts.

"They'll be amazed. Man back from the dead. Rising from the ashes."

I hoped he wasn't going to be disappointed. I understood the way these things worked. Doctors and nurses see a lot of sick people. In. Out. Next. They can't afford to think about them when they go home.

At the first stop in the orthopaedic ward, none of the nurses or registrars that had cared for him were there. We left the lollies on the counter of the nurses' station.

At the second one — the cancer ward — one nurse vaguely recognised him. She made polite conversation for a minute until someone called her name and she excused herself.

In the chemo clinic, the nurse who had mostly administered his drugs, who we had joked with every third Friday for six months, who had discussed travel and movies, had left. Gone overseas again to pursue her own life. The movie vouchers we'd bought her lay unopened on the reception desk. Someone said they'd send them on. Our other nurse was busy in her purple gown, she called out a cheerful hello and we chatted briefly but she was soon swept away by the needs of her patients.

When you finish cancer treatment it's goodbye, you don't make a promise to keep in touch.

Nor do you pop into a cancer clinic for a casual chat. The only reason you go back there is because you have to — you need more treatment.

On the drive home, Kev's mood was slightly flat. No-one had been there to proclaim the miracle.

"They're just getting on with their lives," I tried to explain. "They cared about you. It's just that you were a patient. For every one like you there are a whole lot more that end up in the mortuary. The medical staff do their best, but they don't hold onto the feelings when they leave the hospital. If they did, they couldn't do their job."

He nodded.

"I'm just really grateful for what they did."

"I am too. But a hospital works like a newsroom — just like the newspaper keeps coming out, there's always another patient in the queue."

"I guess so."

I paused. "Hospitals are full of good people doing good work, but it's their work. You can only be truly missed by the people who love you. I'm pretty happy you're still here, you know. I'm all over the miracle.

He smiled. "Then I'm a pretty lucky guy."

"So where are my lollies?"

Chapter 20

THE 19ᵀᴴ HOLE

In golf, the 19th hole is the name given to the clubhouse bar. It's where the players gather for a beer and shot-by-shot analysis of the day's round.

In cancer, the 19th hole was life on the other side of treatment, the place you return to after you're given a pass out from the disease. It's a bit like coming home from a holiday. You unpack the bags, share the photos, bank the memories and then step back on the treadmill.

Except when you've survived cancer your concept of life has changed. Or your view of how much life you've got left. So you don't know whether you want to speed the treadmill up, or slow it down. Or sell it on Trade Me and figure out another way of spending your time.

Does anyone ever *finish* cancer?

At what point do you turn away and say "that's it" — time for the next thing? Or does it always lurk, always colour your life and choices from the first moment it joins your life? I'm not sure. It felt like we'd been away somewhere for eight months and turned up at a different playground with an unfamiliar layout and a bunch of new toys.

Where to start? How to play?

You see, the other side of cancer — of any serious illness — is a wasteland. Science has documented it and my clients have taught me the truth of it. This is where you can really get into trouble, where financial pressures rear up, where relationships run aground and families fall apart, where — while the body struggles forward — the mind can begin to play up.

Cancer survivors, partners, families, friends can all ride the emotional rollercoaster, the trauma of a knock with death: depression, anxiety, anger, guilt, relief, resentment, gratitude, isolation, hopelessness. And everyone is dealing with the fear of IT COMING BACK.

Physically, Kev felt good, "like I've had my windows cleaned," he said.

His three-monthly checkup revealed a clean bill of health: clear chest, abdomen soft, bloods perfect, weight back to baseline. He was tumour free and, aside from itches, rashes, discoloured skin pigments and heavy legs, he was in perfect health.

For now.

"Do you worry?" I asked. He had just heard that one of the guys who was having chemo at the same time had died. Nigel Llewellyn, Kev's buddy from University days who we'd seen on our first day in the chemo clinic, had also died and this was both humbling and upsetting to him.

While he seemed emotionally stable and cheerful, I knew depression was a risk for cancer survivors as they search for meaning in the experience and try to figure out the way forward. I wanted him to talk honestly about how he was feeling: I didn't want him to tuck his thoughts, his fears in his stomach — for obvious reasons.

"There's not a day when I don't think about it," he said quietly.

Then his thoughts poured out. "I worry about the cancer coming back. And if it does, will I have the energy and the optimism to go through the treatment all over again. I worry that I'll be disabled by it, useless to my employers and to my family.

"I worry that if it's terminal, can I be dignified in facing death? I worry about leaving — what I'll miss out on. What will happen to you? The girls? I worry about my family."

I understood. I had my own list, just as long as his. Perhaps most of all I worried that our fear would disable our capacity to live well. I know there is meaning in suffering but it takes a class act to keep rising above it, to keep looking for the gold.

Survivorship, it's called.

And, perversely, it can make having cancer seem like the easy bit. That's because the medical side of treatment comes with a map. People who know more than you tell you where to go and what to do. They book appointments for you. They call you, they send you letters. They answer questions, they explain things. They hold the torch for you, the way is lit.

But when you "survive", you have to go out and buy your own torch. Then you have to pick through the rubble yourself.

With cancer in our wake, it was a time for celebration. Our friend Abby, who'd been living in Australia, returned to share the champagne she'd bought for us five months earlier as a Get Well incentive. The bottle had been sitting on the book shelf, in full view, an enticement to get to the Other Side.

"It's a miracle Norks," she hugged him tightly. "You know the truth? I never thought you'd be here to drink this with me."

"Gee thanks Abbles," he smiled. "I suspect not many people did."

"I think even you had your doubts," she said.

"There were moments."

We raised our glasses. But the joy, the fun, which usually came easily to me, just wasn't there. There were too many pieces to put back together, too many people to take care of, too many emotions to keep in check. As the leader of the Cancer Project, I was exhausted, still obliged to keep monitoring everyone, feeling responsible for their emotional health and wellbeing.

Especially as a psychologist. There was no excuse not to get it right. People expected it of me; I expected it of myself.

"How's Kevin?' people said, everywhere I went.

"How's Kevin?

"How's Kev?

"How's Norks getting on?

Then to me: "Are you back at work yet? How many days a week?" As if a return to work — especially fulltime work — was a marker for recovery, or success. Which it had never been to me, not since the Barbie years, anyway.

"He's so lucky he's had you," other people said. "You would have kept his head straight. You would have known exactly what to do, how to get through this."

In theory, yes. But as I tried to gather all the ragged pieces of our lives, I wasn't so sure. Part of me wanted to run, to run away from it as fast and as far as I could, everything. Italy anyone?

Everyone seemed to expect things were back to normal, but our normal had shifted into an unfamiliar and slightly chilly place. I recalled a woman with a terminal diagnosis telling me about her friend who'd said to her, accusingly: "you've changed since you got cancer."

"Everything about me has changed," she told me. " I was told that I'm going to die. Very soon." she told me. "What was she thinking? Was I really supposed not to change?"

It was true. Everything felt different.

The trauma symptoms — feelings, flashbacks, dark thoughts, anxieties — which follow any threat to life reared up in all of us: Tess's panic when her dad didn't answer her texts quickly (Where was he? Had he collapsed somewhere?), the sudden flare of Kate's eczema, my sitting bolt upright in bed every time Kev went to the toilet in the night because I was so worried about him falling. There was no need for it now, he was fine, but my body remained on high alert; I couldn't stop the physical reaction, I couldn't bring my keyed emotional state down naturally.

It was why I had to be careful with my Sauvignon Blanc intake.

The truth is that when you finally get your ticket out of cancer you don't just swell with love and gratitude and walk out into the sunshine of a bright new day. That's Fantasyland. You want to rejoice, you feel obliged to be happy, but you are still so emotionally shaken that you can't cut loose from it.

You feel tainted, as though cancer has infiltrated every part of you. And — somehow — you have to stop yourself from hating it and begin to let it go so it won't hold you to ransom for the rest of your life.

Out of the blue an old friend called. She and her husband were in town and wanted to meet for a meal. They were a slightly older couple we'd known for 20 years but only see, or talk to, about once a year. Because we don't have any common friends — and I was disinclined to throw our story and updates on Facebook — they'd missed the whole cancer saga.

"We'd love to see you," I said, arranging to meet them at a new Italian restaurant in the city. We were there, seated, when they arrived so they didn't notice Kev's limp. His hair had fully grown back, his body filled out and only the white blotches on his face and hands gave away the damage the chemo drugs had done to the pigment in his skin. In the dimmed lighting, he looked close to the way he did when they last saw him.

They'd had a hard year. Robyn was recovering from a second stroke and now the threat of illness shadowed them the way I didn't want to admit cancer was following us.

She — knowing the increased likelihood of a third stroke and what that might mean for her health and physical function — wanted to travel and live overseas for a few months. Ed, who was traumatised by the impact of the first two strokes and terrified of losing her, wanted to stay home, bank their money and keep things steady.

It had created tension between a couple who had long been role models to us in raising their children while maintaining a healthy, loving relationship.

As the pizzas were rolled out, so was Kev's — our — story. They were shocked — and it led us to talk about how illness messes with relationships.

"God knows what happens to couples who are falling apart before one of them gets sick," Robyn says.

"It's a nightmare," she said to me, as we wandered down the city streets after dinner. We'd broken a few steps away from the boys and we talked — honestly — about how tough it had been all round. I told her about the tears I'd spilled, something I had kept mostly to myself. I could see Kev watching me, craning his head to listen.

"Write about it," she said. "Write about what serious

illness really does to relationships. How relationships go through different stages. Not all that crap about it bringing you closer and making you stronger."

I smiled; Robyn was on a roll. "What doesn't kill you makes you stronger? If I have to hear that line again… hardship, suffering makes you a better person. For God's sake. I was all right before. I didn't need a stroke to take me to a higher place."

I knew what she meant. Post-traumatic growth (PTG) was hot in Positive Psychology circles. The idea was that people could grow and change as the result of highly challenging life circumstances. It was a valid theory but, to be honest, there was a lot of pain to get through first.

So I cast positivity aside for a while and joined in. "I don't like that cancer's made life so much more urgent. Do things now. Write the bucket list. Tick things off. Don't wait. JUST IN CASE. I was a person in a hurry before. I don't need more fire up my ass."

We were both laughing but we were also in unspoken agreement: *We are not greater, or lesser, than we were before. We're just people, trying to wade through the mud of illness.*

Cancer hasn't made me a better person, not at all. It has made me a more wrinkled and less fun one, at least temporarily. I am a *different* person, though, and a more empathetic psychologist. Any experience that pushes you to the edge of the cliff helps you understand the frailties of the human condition. It fills you out, emotionally, and that is surely a good thing. You have to be able to find your way back though; that's the hard, scary bit.

In the car on the way home, Kev and I continued the conversation.

"Wow, it's been hard for them," he said.

I nodded. A silent acknowledgement, perhaps, that our relationship was under threat. On the outside, we were the couple who survived, the bonds of our love strengthened by adversity. On the inside, it was not like that at all. We were just another couple slapped by our mortality, fractured by cancer, unsure about how to move forward.

Both now fully conscious of the brevity of life, questions hung.

Should we proceed with caution, savouring whatever time we have left? Or should we go hard: throw our money at a sports car, rip down the roof and floor the pedal?

Like many couples traumatised by illness, Kev and I wanted different things. Naturally restless, I wanted to go a little crazy, try things, travel, bleed dry whatever time we had left. I was too scared to commit to a lease on another office in case it all went crazy again (read: the cancer comes back). Kev, always more steady and predictable, was just thrilled to be alive. He was grateful to be able to put one foot in front of the other. He could hardly walk, he couldn't travel far offshore because he was such a high insurance risk. He had his family and his work and his mates and his golf cart. That was his bliss. But me — I could see a thousand nights in front of television stretching out in front of me and I felt cross-eyed with boredom.

"We need to talk," I said.

He looked at me and laughed. He knew me better than I credited him for.

"Where do you want to go?" he said.

I breathed out, with relief. It was not so much about going somewhere, it was knowing things were possible, knowing that I could. Knowing that he knew it too.

"Let's set some goals. Some joint ones. Things we both want to do."

"Thanks," I said.

Then he looked at me, a crooked smile spread across his face. "I didn't know you cried."

"You shouldn't have been listening. That was a girl thing."

"I can't believe you cried. For me."

"Don't get carried away," I volleyed back, feeling an unfamiliar rush of emotion — not quite joy, but possibility. "Not all the tears were for you. Most of them were self pity."

Chapter 21

THE CLUTCH PLAYER

My cellphone shrilled one morning before the 6am alarm went off. I snatched at it, the way you do when you've been sleeping poorly and mentally on edge for 10 months, my heart in my mouth, mentally accounting for each member of my family: Kev, in bed beside me; Tess, in the next room. Kate? Safe in her flat? My parents?

We were a couple of months into Kev's remission. Outwardly relaxed, moving on. Inwardly fragile. Afraid of what lay ahead.

On the end of the line was Aaron Klee, the then manager of one of my clients, calling to give me a heads-up before I flipped on the radio. Jesse Ryder had been in a scuffle outside a bar in Christchurch, cracked his head in a fall and was now lying in intensive care in a medically-induced coma.

"It's touch and go," Klee said and I felt my stomach knot up.

Ryder was an international cricketer of bad-boy reputation, who I'd worked with for five years. I don't usually name my clients when writing or speaking about my work but Jesse and I had been outed in the media a year earlier and we had both since publicly acknowledged our working relationship.

It had been quite a journey: injury, alcohol, conflict, a self-imposed exile from cricket. A trip to India together in 2012 when he opened the batting for the Pune Warriors in the Indian Premier League (IPL). An investigation after testing positive for using a banned substance (later thrown out as genuine error though he was still given a six-month suspension). Other things, too. Personal stories, not mine to reveal.

I cared. I wanted to see him.

He'd come out of his coma with his girlfriend and whanau around him. A couple of days later I was sitting alone in his hospital room, my feet up on the end of his bed, when he woke. Seeing me, he began to rant about urinating into a catheter tube.

"This thing's such a shit," he said. Then "do you want a jetplane?" As though catheter tubes and lollies were perfectly suited in the same sentence.

I took a couple of sweets and we talked. There seemed a

lot to say. His sense of humour was still there: he'd always been the master of the one-liner, especially when it gently targeted me.

I reflected on how far we'd come from those early days when he sat almost mute on my couch and kept his cap down over his eyes for months so he wouldn't have to look at me.

We'd connected through our shared Iwi and honed our relationship over many hours — but it was at the driving range where we did our best work. I'd suggested meeting there so we had something physical to do while we talked. It was a good strategy for working with young men: they could talk freely without having to make eye contact. There, smashing golf balls, he began to open up.

The golf sessions were fiercely competitive too. We'd take turns at dreaming up contests. Straightest drive, nearest the pin over various distances, best short iron, prettiest shot.

"Prettiest shot?" he'd said, frowning at one of my suggestions. "That's a bit desperate isn't it?"

"Well I'm not going to take you on at longest drive." A natural left-hander, he could smack the ball 300 yards off the tee. He could hit it nearly as far with a right-handed club.

One day the contest was particularly tight and we went to the putting green, the score locked at six points-all. The outcome came down to the last putt, both from the edge of the green. I missed mine and Jesse knocked his in from 20 feet, throwing his ball in the air and whooping in victory as I complained of unfair advantage: "No need to gloat. You should beat me. You're twice my size and half my age."

"It's how you play in the clutch, Karen," he said, cutting me no slack at all. "Next time bring your A game."

I had smiled, because it was exactly what I would have told him. A clutch player could be counted on to achieve in a critical situation — or in the nick of time. We'd talked about it: how the best athletes rise up under pressure.

Now he lay on the other side of a coma, unaware of how close he may have come to death, confused at the amount of caring heaped on him by email, texts and tweets from all over the world.

His skin was an odd ivory colour and he rubbed at his forehead to ease the pounding inside his head. It seemed a long way from this bed back to the cricket pitch, the place where he felt most relaxed, most safe.

"You'll be back Jess," I said, helping myself to another jetplane.

He just stared at me, one dark eyebrow slightly raised, the blank look I'd come to know as the mask for most of his emotions: anger, sadness fear, even happiness.

"You're a clutch player, remember." I went on. "Tough under the pump. It'll take more than this to end your career. "

He still said nothing, always uncomfortable with talking about his strengths. We sat in easy silence for a few moments.

"How's your husband? Jesse said suddenly, as if reading my thoughts. He'd known of Kev's cancer because I'd had to juggle appointments and cancel on him a couple of times. But he didn't know any details.

"He's good, thanks. It's been hard though. He nearly died, he's got a golf cart now because he still can't walk too well. But what do you do? Life's not easy sometimes."

He nodded. Then he spoke with his own special brand of insight, one that occasionally caught me off guard and reminded me why my clients sometimes helped me more than I helped them.

"Then it's lucky you're a clutch player too," he said.

*"There's a crack in everything.
That's how the light gets in."*

*Leonard Cohen
Anthem*

Chapter 22

PICKING UP THE BALLS

Just like at the driving range, the balls were everywhere.

That's the job after any trauma isn't it? To pick up the scattered balls, to place them back on the tee, to begin again.

There wasn't an aspect of our lives that hadn't been slapped around by cancer. Our home, our kids, our friends, our families. Our work, our finances. Our emotions, our health. Our view of each other. Our future. Our love.

We didn't need it. Who does?

Over the next few months, we picked up most of the balls. We went back to work, we planned a holiday, we invested time into our kids and our families. Kev and his mum talked fully about the painful death of his sister, the truth of how it happened and how it had affected them both. She gave him Colleen's Baptism gift — a gold brooch inscribed with her name — which made him cry.

We nursed Tommy, our old dog, through his own cancer until he had to be put down. We slowed down, we tried not to sweat the small stuff. We threw out the clothes Kev had worn when he was sick, I stopped being too scared to go away with my friends for a night. We removed all pill bottles from sight; we planned to paint and renovate the living room which seemed to carry the stench of illness in its walls. I finally took his emergency blood identification card out of my wallet, less fearful he'd be rushed to hospital with a life-threatening infection.

But, as they say in golf, the yips remain.

Sometimes, we have bad dreams.

Sometimes, we worry. Each cough or cold or unexplained burst of pain sends a ripple of alarm, one that we force ourselves to treat calmly. Each three monthly check up is another notch on the odometer, another exhalation of breath as the all-clear is given.

Our kids, too, bear the scars of cancer.

Tess panicked when we told her we were going out for dinner at an upmarket restaurant in case it meant we had bad news (actually we had a free voucher). Kate told her dad she considered having a child quickly so he would have the chance to be a granddad. Both of them have experienced related anxieties. I still feel my heart race whenever I wake in the night to an empty space in the bed.

And, occasionally, the lump in my throat, the ball of dread in my stomach, just won't break up and go away.

So you see? Everyone is a little banged up by the experience.

There's a quote I have always liked from the character Pip, in Charles Dickens' classic novel *Great Expectations*.

"That was a memorable day for me, for it made great changes in me. But, it is the same with any life. Imagine one selected day struck out of it and think how different its course would have been. Pause…and think for a moment of the long chain of iron or gold, of thorns or flowers, that would never have bound you, but for the formation of the first link on one memorable day."

It's true, isn't it?

In any life, certain days and dates become the first links in the chains. You hope they will be chains of gold or flowers but they can't all be. Sometimes the chains are made of iron. Sometimes, thorns.

So it was with cancer.

July 16, the day of Kev's diagnosis.

It was just a date, a marker, but suddenly it loomed large, threatening all the other significant dates that formed the chains of our lives.

Both Kev and I knew the first anniversary of his diagnosis was coming, but we didn't say anything to each other. It was like playing chicken. Who would blink first?

"Do you want to go out for dinner?" he finally said a couple of days before.

I shook my head. "I don't really want to celebrate cancer. Do you?

"No. I want to ignore it. Let's go out the night after."

"Loving your mental state."

He grinned. "Cancer's not going to rule us. I'll get you a wine."

Four days later, it was to be Tess's birthday. She'd asked for a party to replace the wild ride we'd had for her 18th up in the hospital ward.

"There won't be any vomiting in the bushes this year," she promised. "You're lucky! We're a whole year older."

Then, quietly to me, "let's hope Kevvo doesn't mess it up this year with his attention seeking behaviour."

Suddenly she grew serious, walking over to Kev's chair and sitting on the couch next to him.

"Can we talk?"

We held our breath. Teenagers announcing they want to talk usually means there is something big on the agenda. Drugs. Alcohol. Moving out. Pregnancy. Emotionally I cowered and felt myself inhale. Kev leaned back in his chair.

"It's like this guys."

We waited.

"Do you think we could we put a door back on the bathroom? For the party? My friends find the whole curtain thing creepy. You can't lock it — and you can hear people. What they're doing in there."

Was that it?

We waited a little more.

"Well? It's not the third world. People have doors on bathrooms here."

We started to laugh. The flapping navy bathroom door curtain had become a fixture. We'd almost forgotten it.

"Fair request. It's your birthday. We'll get you a door."

"Happiness is Love. Full Stop."

George Valiant, Principal Investigator

The five-word conclusion to The Grant Study, a 75-year longitudinal study by Harvard Medical School

Chapter 23

LET'S GO SHOPPING

Kev and I were walking down Willis Street in the city one Saturday morning, in search of a coffee. He was walking freely again, he said it felt like a mixture of concrete and pins and needles in his legs and feet but — still — we were once again a mobile couple, in town, doing ordinary things.

Things to be grateful for: Coffee. Walking. Together.

The following week he was to cover the Royal Tour, the visit to New Zealand by the Duke and Duchess of Cambridge and baby Prince George. It was the young Royal family's first gig on the world stage and the media attention promised to be huge.

Kev had reported on plenty of big events, but Royal watching was missing from his CV. He was excited, but playing it down. There were factions in the journalism world who thought it was uncool to be excited about covering a Royal Tour. Privately, he was worried his legs wouldn't hold up for all the standing and walking required, but he was itching to do it.

"What are you going to wear?" I asked, suddenly. He'd been back at work for a while and his suits looked baggy and dated. Or perhaps the change in his body shape had done them out of a job.

"Clothes? No idea. Don't care. I'm a man."

"What do you reckon we get you a new suit?"

He shrugged, disinterested. He hated trying on clothes.

"I mean you're not going to die now so it wouldn't be a waste of money. A few months ago — no. But now I reckon we can justify it."

He looked at me oddly then, head on one side.

"What's wrong?" I said, trying not to smile. "I just think you're going to live long enough to make the spend worthwhile."

He shook his head, at the same time throwing an arm around my shoulder. I jumped as he lurched towards me. But it was a carefree gesture — not one of a man who had lost his balance and was in free fall towards the pavement.

I didn't need to catch him. I really didn't.

His face split into a wide grin.

"I love it," he said. "Let's go shopping."

ONE MORE THING

A year into Kev's remission, I signed up to run a 10km race. I'd done a handful of these races before but this time I'd done only minimal training; I was just doing it to throw another peg in the ground as we edged forward, to keep my own mental health on track.

Kev was there in the crowd on this mid-winter day, coaching, yelling encouragement, unable to see me amongst the masses crawling along Wellington's waterfront. I rounded the halfway cone but, by the 6km mark, I was struggling, breathing heavily with my stomach stitching up.

"Come on. Use your rat-like cunning," I muttered, drawing on Kev's running philosophy to urge myself on. I shuffled in behind a young man in a pink sweater, using him as a windbreak. But my inner rat had bailed. It was just plain hard work. With nothing left for the sprint home, I plodded across the finish line, a few minutes outside my best time. It was a fair, even respectable, result for my age and the training I've done but, still, I'm competitive — I was disappointed.

Running finds you out, I recalled Kev saying. It pays you back exactly what you put in.

Life too, I thought, entering the exit tunnel.

In and Out. Give and Take.

It's a fair deal. So while you're still alive you'd better deliver on your side of the bargain. Smiling, I grabbed a banana and walked out to meet my cheer team of one.

My husband, my caddy.

For whatever lies ahead.

THE END

A ROADMAP FOR CANCER

There are no guarantees in cancer. There is no foolproof plan for getting to the other side. If there was someone would have packaged it, sold it for millions, and be lying in a hammock somewhere in the sun sipping a cocktail. I wish.

When cancer came calling we were well looked after medically. The rest was in our hands. There was no roadmap to provide quick and accurate guidance through cancer. There was no checklist for keeping our thinking straight and our minds in the game. We had to figure it out ourselves.

This is what we learned; this is the best of what we know:

- MOBILISE. Mind, body and spirit have to move in the same direction. When you find out you, or someone you love, has cancer, move quickly. Make a plan and do something. If you can't think straight, or you are too shocked to make a plan, just do one thing to get things started.

- CHOOSE YOUR TREATMENT PLAN CAREFULLY. Ask questions, make an informed decision, then go with it. Believing in your plan (and having your family on board too) is a key part of your recovery.

- GET DRESSED EVERY DAY. (Shave or apply makeup if that's what you would normally do). Pyjamas and gowns are for the ill and dying. As often as you can, put your clothes on. It helps to make things normal, to hold firm your place in the world.

- LIE WHEN PEOPLE ASK HOW YOU ARE. Ok, don't lie — but keep it brief. Unless they are health professionals or loved ones, people don't need to know all the details of your disease or the truth of how you are feeling. The more you repeat those details, the more you will stay in the cancer zone. Answer as brightly and positively as you can. It will help keep your own head straight too.

- KEEP IT NORMAL. As often as possible and without exhausting yourself, do normal things: work, cook, socialise. Don't step out of the world; stay connected to it. Plan to do something on chemo/treatment days — it helps remind you that there is life DURING chemo/treatment.

- BUILD YOUR TEAM. Know the half dozen people you can really count on to help you. Know who's fully in your corner and let them in, let them help you. Talk to them. If you are lonely in your experience a mental health professional or cancer support group can help.

- TREAT YOURSELF. This one is especially for caregivers and partners. Look after your own needs, health and wellbeing. You are the most important person/people on the team.

- LANGUAGE MATTERS. Refer to cancer as cancer, not as the big C. Don't be afraid to use the word and **never** give it a capital C — you'll be handing over the power. Do not talk about the cancer FIGHT or the BATTLE; be tough and resolute but don't go to war with it. Cancer will beat you.

- CANCER PROs. Write a list of all the things you have to be grateful for. If this is too difficult or seems too big just write down three things every evening. Do it every day, it'll help balance your negative thoughts and keep your head straight.

- LAUGHTER AND PETS. Both are good therapy. Seek fun, watch funny movies — even if you don't feel like it. If you don't have a pet, find a way to be around animals. (Provided you like animals!)

- IMPROVE NUTRITION. There is lots of personal choice available here. You don't have to fill yourself with green juice and go vegan BUT you do have to make sensible choices, increase your intake of naturally grown and fresh foods and be moderate with alcohol and fatty foods. If you are overweight, more extreme measures are required. Cut out processed sugar — it is said to feed tumours. Even if it doesn't, it's not good for you.

- EXERCISE. This is a non-negotiable. Move whatever body parts you can. Try to get your heart rate up sometimes. At the very least, do some static exercises, walk and go outside — get fresh air regularly.

- QUIET THE CHAOS. Know yourself and your cancer story. Make peace with old wounds. Understand your vulnerabilities and what makes you stressed. Find ways to relax, to turn off the internal noise. Some people find meditation and yoga helpful; but music, walking, art, writing, crafts and — you guessed it — golf can all help.

- STRUCTURE YOUR DAYS. Make a plan for the day the night before (write down the five things you plan to do the next day). Do not wake up not having a clue what the day will hold. Your mind will play tricks on you.

- INTERNET. Stay off! Searching your symptoms and prognosis is a sure fire way to drive up your fear when you are already vulnerable. If you have questions ask health professionals — or get someone else to look things up for you on REPUTABLE websites.

- DO, DON'T THINK. When your mind travels into dark places (and it will), haul it back and distract yourself with an activity. Simple active things: a shower, a crossword, some craft activity, reading may work best. Mobile activities are handy too; keep something in your bag or pocket.

- SHORT TERM GOALS. Plan and write down little things you can look forward to. It doesn't matter how small the goal, it's important to have things out in front to move towards.

- STAY CONNECTED. Withdrawing socially and becoming isolated is a trap. Work if you can, play and be with others when you can. Talk to other people (not just about your cancer) — about their lives, what they are doing and planning. Remember that people who don't have cancer have problems too.

- CELEBRATE. Even when things are tough, there are always tiny things that can be celebrated. Look for them and get your support team to help.

- CHANGE. Make some changes to the way you lived and operated before. Assess your lifestyle. You might need to slow down or reassess your priorities and relationships. Psychologically it is very important to send yourself a mental signal that you are doing things differently.

- JOURNEY, NOT DESTINATION. Focus on what you have to do — not where your cancer experience will end. You can't control the outcome but you can do everything along the way to influence it.

- JUST THIS DAY. This is the most important thing of all. When you are going through cancer this is the only thing you can be certain of. Life is just a series of moments. Focus on living the moments and the days as well as you can.

- HOPE. Stay in the game. Keep a visual symbol of hope where you can see it. And even if your own future is uncertain find hope in your contribution to others.

- ACCEPTANCE. Of cancer and all that it brought with it. Of the loss of what you had. Of the changes in your world. This can be a hard place to get to but keep trying. It will bring you peace.